THE WORLD OF TOMORROW

also by tom tomorrow

THE WORLD OF TOMORROW

by tom tomorrow

First Printing, September 2012
ISBN-13: 978-1-936561-73-5

10 9 8 7 6 5 4 3 2 1
Printed in Canada

Published by **TopatoCo Books,**
a division of **The Topato Corporation.**
116 Pleasant St. Ste 203
Easthampton, MA 01027

thismodernworld.com
topatoco.com

I am profoundly indebted to the fine folks at TopatoCo. Jeffrey Rowland has been an enthusiastic collaborator on books and t-shirts and toys, and we haven't even been working together a full year yet. And many thanks are due David Malki for his superlative layout and design work on the book you now hold.

Heartfelt thanks also to Ed Vedder, who always goes above and beyond. It is a genuine privilege to call him a friend.

Love and gratitude to my wife, Beverly, who is always there to help talk out an idea, or just as often to provide one of her own. She is my unindicted co-conspirator, and she is remarkable.

This book is dedicated to Nicholas, who will live in the actual world of tomorrow.

introduction

WE'RE TRIBAL CREATURES, WE HUMAN BEINGS. We divide the world into teams, and root for our own. When somebody on "our" team wins an election, then it's time to put on the cheerleading uniform and pull out the pom-poms, and if we are troubled by nagging contradictions or disappointments or outright betrayals, we construct intricate, beautiful, and utterly implausible rationalizations to explain it all away—because we want to root for our team, even when our team is doing things which would utterly outrage us, were they done by the *other* team.

Except that's not how satire works. Satire is about probing the spots that bother you, whether they're conveniently partisan or not. Satire is about acknowledging the contradictions and disappointments. When satire is walking down the road and comes across rationalizations as flimsy as a house of cards, satire takes a deep breath and blows them the hell down. Satire based in partisanship rather than truth is not satire at all, but rather propaganda, and there's a reason propagandists are only slightly more well regarded than child molesters in this society.

This is not to say that satire never takes sides, particularly when one side is clearly out of its freaking mind. But when one side is certifiably insane, and the other is blathering on about "working together to get things done," well, satire gets impatient.

If you see where I'm going with this.

Satire in the age of Obama has been a tricky balancing act. There's the fact that the Republicans have gone increasingly off the deep end, which makes them an easy target for satire, almost irresistible. (Satire is truthful, but not always immune to temptation.) But that doesn't mean that Democrats are off the hook, particularly when you have an administration which has embraced and in some cases surpassed many of the worst elements of its predecessors: warrantless wiretapping, indefinite detention, and the continuation of wars which should have ended long ago—hell, which never should have been started in the first place.

But we're tribal creatures, and people don't like seeing their own side questioned. So you get the endless, intricate rationalizations. You are told the presidency of the most powerful nation on Earth is actually one of the most powerless offices ever devised by man; that the true power resides with the Congress, while the president is actually little more than a figurehead. You are told that what appears to be an embrace of Republican ideals, such as cutting Social Security and Medicare, is actually part of an elaborate feint designed to trick the other side into defeating themselves, a multi-dimensional chess game played by a master of ju-jitsu. You are told that it's too soon to criticize, the president has only been in office six months, a year, three and a half years, a single term.

You are told that *any* criticism of the first black president is, by definition, racist.

And you say, fuck that shit.

And yet, satire in the age of Obama is also satire in the age of the Tea Party, and Michele Bachmann, Sarah Palin and Fox News and Newt Gingrich (momentarily) resurgent, and climate denialism and gun lunacy and "legitimate rape" and all rest of the sheer crazy right-wing noise-machine babble. You don't want to let the Democrats off the hook, or make excuses for them, but every time you turn around the Republicans are doing something so head-explodingly hypocritical and/or stupid and/or venal and/or destructive to society as we know it that it's hard to find a way to say everything you're desperately trying to say, to fit it all into six panels in a single weekly cartoon.

The cartoons in this book cover the time span roughly from August, 2010 through August, 2012, and I hope they mostly live up to what satire should be. Of course the problem with that particular timeframe is that as I write these words, as the publishers and I prepare to ship these files off to the printer, I have no idea whether the next president will be the technocratic moderate with a disturbing indifference to civil liberties, or the blandly dishonest rich guy with the Ayn Rand acolyte for a running mate. Hope that works out for you, people of the future!—along with the economy and the increasingly malevolent climate and any number of other problems that any reasonably bright twelve-year-old could have seen coming five miles off in the distance on a cloudy day, but which we collectively ignored until our economy went careening into the gutter and our weather started trying to kill us at every opportunity, and it just wasn't a normal week in America if a half dozen people weren't gunned down in some random massacre—at which point, we took a decisive breath and continued to look the other way. Because that's how our political system works in the year 2012.

But I'm an optimist. I figure, when the surface of the planet is a dystopian hellscape rendered mostly uninhabitable by drought and firestorms, and the sacred cult of austerity has driven the unemployment rate up to 95%, and we all live in fear that some Too Gigantic To Fail megabank will repossess the cardboard boxes and plastic trash bags with which we try to protect ourselves from the raging elements—I figure at that point, then maybe we'll realize we've really got to start thinking about someday trying to figure out a way to deal with some of these problems. Maybe.

Ha ha! I kid, of course. At that point, only the very richest among us will be able to afford cardboard boxes! But that's all a problem for another day, which is to say, tomorrow. And the World of Tomorrow is *always* a day away.

So for today, enjoy these cartoons. They are dispatches from an era of precipitous decline, a weekly contemporaneous history of a society's gradual descent into madness. Readers frequently describe my work as "depressingly accurate," or say that they would laugh if they weren't busy crying. I say, fuck that! Laugh anyway, because in the long run laughter is all we have. Apart from, you know, our families, and our health, and whatever meager savings we might have after the vultures of Wall Street are through picking our carcasses clean. But you get the idea. Laughter's a necesary corrective. And while I'm frequently impotent with rage in the face of so much I can't even begin to solve, laughter's the thing I've got and can pass on to you. It's not a lot, but it's what I have.

If you ask me, it's better to light a candle *and* curse the darkness.

Thanks for reading.

—Dan Perkins
(Tom Tomorrow)
New Haven, Connecticut
August, 2012

foreword

I HAVE KNOWN DAN PERKINS FOR MANY YEARS now. However, not half as long as I've known Tom Tomorrow.

My initial reaction upon meeting Dan was one of intimidation, as I had been a dedicated follower of his potent, political cartoon strips for over a decade. I had no idea at the time that he would become such an extraordinary friend. Compassionate and kind. Hysterically funny, yet still brooding. All of this while still retaining his iconic stature.

It has been quite remarkable to have a compatriot who works so hard in the trenches. One who is outspoken and true to all the ideals that you both share. Sometimes in conversation we will compare jobs. I write a song or piece of music when I feel the need. Or when the song comes. In comparison, Dan digs in at it every week without fail. Compiling thought and information, all current and immaculately precise. And thus, prolific! I am often amazed when I realize that not only is every episode packed with multi-layered meaning, but that a single square or thought bubble is never wasted. That is the point where I bow down to his genius.

He works hard. I'm so grateful to be one of the many who benefit from his wit and focus.

Not a provocateur. He is a reporter exposing underlying truths, or sometimes truths which are lying on the surface with no one taking notice.

In our current and ever-changing media world, there are more people reading Dan's cartoons than ever before, all over the world—but fewer places willing, or able, to pay for them. To think that this powerful form of social commentary (that we often take for granted) could be lost is a real tragedy.

I am proud to present this latest compilation of Dan's view regarding *This Modern World.*

Long live Tom Tomorrow.

Long live tomorrow.

—Eddie Vedder
Seattle, Washington
August, 2012

THIS MODERN WORLD

by TOM TOMORROW

THEY DENIED REALITY.

GLOBAL WARMING IS A LIBERAL *HOAX!*

SARAH PALIN IS *TOTALLY* QUALIFIED TO BE PRESIDENT!

THEY DISTORTED REALITY.

THE DEMOCRAT PARTY HAS ONLY ONE GOAL-- TO *DESTROY AMERICA!*

WE'RE ON THE ROAD TO A *SOCIALIST TAKEOVER!*

THEY REWROTE REALITY.

GEORGE W. BUSH WASN'T A *REAL* CONSERVATIVE!

BARACK OBAMA ISN'T A *REAL* AMERICAN CITIZEN!

IN WAYS BIG AND SMALL, CONSERVATIVES UNDERMINED THE VERY CONCEPT OF REALITY--UNTIL ONE DAY REALITY COULD NO LONGER STAND THE STRAIN.

KER-RAAASSSSSH!

URK.

UH OH.

HUMANS WERE SUDDENLY ADRIFT IN A UNIVERSE DEVOID OF HISTORY AND SCIENCE... A PLACE WHERE RATIONALITY HELD NO SWAY.

THE FOUNDING FATHERS *NEVER* INTENDED TO SEPARATE CHURCH AND STATE!

AND THEY WERE 17 FEET TALL AND HAD ADAMANTIUM BONES!

NEEDLESS TO SAY, MANY PEOPLE FOUND IT ALL EXTREMELY DISTURBING.

WITHOUT THE MOST FUNDAMENTAL CONSENSUS REALITY--HOW CAN SOCIETY *FUNCTION?*

SOME DAYS YOU JUST CAN'T HOLD ONTO YOUR *HEAD!*

DANGER WILL ROBINSON!

BUT MOST CONSERVATIVES FELT PERFECTLY AT HOME.

WOO HOO! SARAH PALIN *IS* QUALIFIED TO BE PRESIDENT!

AND MONKEYS *CAN* FLY OUT OF BODILY ORIFICES!

REALITY ALWAYS *WAS* OVERRATED, IF YOU ASK *ME!*

I

THIS MODERN WORLD

by TOM TOMORROW

Panel 1: ON **OUR** EARTH, WINGNUTS PROFESS OUTRAGE OVER THE SO-CALLED "GROUND ZERO MOSQUE."

A VISITOR TO THAT HALLOWED GROUND **MIGHT** WANDER SEVERAL BLOCKS NORTH PAST THE NEIGHBORHOOD STRIP CLUBS, OFF TRACK BETTING PARLOR AND FAST FOOD JOINTS--AND STUMBLE ACROSS AN **ISLAMIC CULTURAL CENTER!**

I'M OFFENDED JUST **THINKING** ABOUT IT!

Panel 2: ON **PARALLEL** EARTH, THEY TAKE IT A STEP FURTHER.

YOU KNOW, THE WHOLE **ISLAND** OF MANHATTAN IS FULL OF MUSLIMS AND OTHER FOREIGN-LOOKING TYPES!

NOT TO MENTION **LIBERALS!**

THEIR VERY **PRESENCE** DEFILES THE MEMORY OF NINE-ELEVEN, IF YOU ASK **ME!**

Panel 3: PARALLEL POLITICAL OPPORTUNISTS ESCALATE THE CRAZY.

THIS BLASPHEMECRATION OF SACROSANCTIFIED GROUND IS **ABHORRENTIBLE!**

I **REFUDIATE** IT **UNEQUIVOCALUTELY!**

Panel 4: IT'S **SHOCKINGLY** INSENSITIVE! DON'T THESE NEW YORKERS UNDERSTAND WHAT GROUND ZERO MEANS TO **REAL** AMERICANS?

Panel 5: DEMOCRATS QUICKLY CAVE.

LET ME STATE CLEARLY THAT PEOPLE HAVE A RIGHT TO LIVE AND WORK IN MANHATTAN--

--BUT I'M NOT SAYING THEY **SHOULD.**

IT WOULD BE **BETTER** IF THEY LIVED AND WORKED ELSEWHERE.

Panel 6: AND EVENTUALLY...

I CAN'T **BELIEVE** THAT EVERYONE HAS TO ABANDON THE ISLAND OF MANHATTAN **ENTIRELY!**

WELL, IF SOME RIGHT WING NUTJOBS ARE OFFENDED--WHAT OTHER CHOICE DO WE **HAVE?**

LAST TRAIN OUT! ALL **ABOOOAAARD!**

Panel 7: NEXT: PARALLEL WINGNUTS FINALLY GET THE NEW YORK CITY OF THEIR DREAMS.

I **LOVE** NEW YORK LAND! IT'S SO CLEAN AND MONOCULTURAL!

THE BRAVERY OF THE AUDIO-ANIMATRONIC FIRST RESPONDERS IS **SO** INSPIRATIONAL!

CAN WE RIDE THE NINE-ELEVEN MEMORIAL **ROLLER COASTER?**

TOM TOMORROW ©2010...www.thismodernworld.com...twitter.com/tomtomorrow

2

THIS MODERN WORLD

by TOM TOMORROW

THIS MODERN WORLD

by TOM TOMORROW

Panel 1: IF MARTIN LUTHER KING WERE ALIVE TODAY, HE WOULD BE A MEMBER OF THE TEA PARTY.

HERE WE GO...

Panel 2: *HE* BELIEVED IN JUDGING PEOPLE BY THE CONTENT OF THEIR CHARACTER--

--NOT THE COLOR OF THEIR SKIN, YES, YES, I KNOW. THAT'S THE ONLY M.L.K. QUOTE ANY CONSERVATIVE SEEMS TO KNOW.

Panel 3: THE TRUTH IS, IF M.L.K. WERE ALIVE TODAY, RIGHT-WINGERS WOULD BE RELEASING FAKE VIDEOS AND GINNING UP STUPID CONTROVERSIES AND GENERALLY DOING EVERYTHING POSSIBLE TO DISCREDIT AND DESTROY HIM.

Panel 4: DID YOU KNOW THAT M.L.K. ADVOCATED NATIONAL HEALTH CARE AND A GUARANTEED INCOME FOR ALL AMERICANS? THAT HE WAS AN ANTI-WAR RADICAL WHO CONSIDERED AMERICA "THE GREATEST PURVEYOR OF VIOLENCE IN THE WORLD TODAY"?

Panel 5: YOU TEA PARTIERS WANT TO PORTRAY *OBAMA* AS A SOCIALIST? AS MY FRIEND ROY EDROSO SAYS, COMPARED TO M.L.K., OBAMA LOOKS LIKE *BARRY GOLDWATER!*

Panel 6: IF MARTIN LUTHER KING WERE ALIVE TODAY, HE WOULD BE APPALLED BY YOUR SCURRILOUS ATTEMPTS TO CO-OPT HIS PROUD CONSERVATIVE LEGACY.

I'M GOING TO GO POUND MY HEAD AGAINST THE WALL NOW.

MAY I JOIN YOU?

TOM TOMORROW © 2010...www.thismodernworld.com...twitter.com/tomtomorrow

4

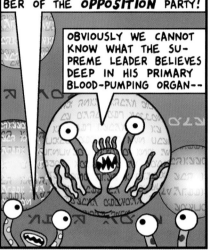
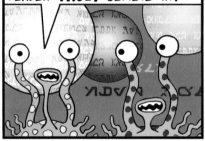

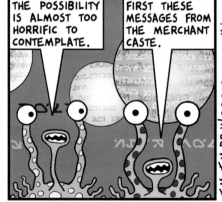

THIS MODERN WORLD

by TOM TOMORROW

Panel 1:

ON *PARALLEL* EARTH, THE BILLIONAIRE BACKERS OF THE TEA PARTY* GROW UNCOMFORTABLE WITH ITS SPORADICALLY POPULIST RHETORIC...AND DECIDE TO FUND A *SPINOFF* PARTY, DEVOTED EVEN *MORE* BLATANTLY TO THE PRIORITIES OF THE EXTREMELY RICH--

THE TEA-AND-CRUMPETS PARTY

*TO READ MORE ABOUT THE BILLIONAIRE BACKERS OF THE TEA PARTY ON *OUR* EARTH, SEE THE 8-30-10 ISSUE OF THE NEW YORKER.

Panel 2:

THE TEA-AND-*CRUMPETS* PARTY DOESN'T EVEN *BOTHER* TRYING TO JUSTIFY ITS OPPOSITION TO ENVIRONMENTAL REGULATIONS!

WE ARE WILLING MOUTHPIECES FOR OIL BILLIONAIRES--PURE AND SIMPLE!

YOU HAVE NO *IDEA* WHAT A RELIEF IT IS, TO STOP PRETENDING TO BE IGNORANT DOOFUSES WHO DON'T BELIEVE IN GLOBAL WARMING!

Panel 3:

NOR DO THEY RESORT TO CRACKPOT CONSPIRACY THEORIES ABOUT *HEALTH CARE REFORM!*

FOR CHRISSAKES, OF *COURSE* WE'RE NOT WORRIED ABOUT A SOCIALIST TAKEOVER! DO WE *LOOK* STUPID?

WE JUST THINK THIS *MIGHT* LEAD TO HIGHER TAXES FOR OUR WEALTHY BENEFACTORS-- AND WE CAN'T RISK *THAT!*

Panel 4:

THEY ARE SIMILARLY FREE TO OPPOSE THE EXTENSION OF UNEMPLOYMENT BENEFITS--

--DESPITE THE LIKELIHOOD IN THIS ECONOMY THAT WE *OURSELVES* WILL SOMEDAY NEED THOSE VERY BENEFITS!

JUST *THINKING* ABOUT TRYING TO RATIONALIZE THAT ONE MAKES *MY* HEAD HURT!

Panel 5:

AND OF COURSE THEIR STANCE ON NET NEUTRALITY BEGINS TO MAKE A LITTLE MORE SENSE AS WELL.

IF WE WERE *ACTUALLY* GRASSROOTS ACTIVISTS, WE'D OBVIOUSLY BENEFIT FROM THE CURRENT MODEL OF THE INTERNET AS AN OPEN PLAYING FIELD.

BUT WE ARE NOT. AND THERE ARE CORPORATE PROFITS AT STAKE.

SO THERE YOU GO.

Panel 6:

THE TEA-AND-*CRUMPETS* PARTY: JUST LIKE THE REGULAR TEA PARTY, ONLY MORESO!

WE'D RATHER LIVE IN A WORLD WITHOUT STREETLIGHTS OR BASIC EMERGENCY SERVICES THAN ASK THE WEALTHY TO RETURN TO CLINTON-ERA LEVELS OF TAXATION!

YOU SEE, WE'RE NOT RICH--BUT WE MIGHT BE *SOMEDAY!*

IN THE MEANTIME WE DON'T WANT BILLIONAIRES TO SUFFER UNDULY.

TOM TOMORROW © 2010....www.thismodernworld.com....twitter.com/tomtomorrow

THIS MODERN WORLD

by TOM TOMORROW

THE CONTINUING ADVENTURES OF
CONSERVATIVE JONES
BOY DETECTIVE

MOONBAT! COME IN! YOU'RE JUST IN TIME FOR THE SOLUTION TO MY *LATEST CASE!*

YOU KNOW, I REALLY WISH YOU'D STOP CALLING ME THAT.

SILENCE, MOONBAT! I MUST MAINTAIN MY LASER-LIKE FOCUS ON THE MATTER AT HAND--THE MYSTERY OF *LIBERAL INDIFFERENCE* TO THE MENACE OF *SHARIA LAW!*

NO LESS AN AUTHORITY THAN *NEWT GINGRICH* HAS RECENTLY WARNED US OF THE THREAT SHARIA POSES TO OUR VERY WAY OF LIFE! SO *WHY* HAVE LIBERALS BEEN SO QUIET? IS IT BECAUSE THEY SECRETLY *SUPPORT* THE OBJECTIVES OF THE *TALIBAN?!*

NO. NO, IT IS NOT.

WHAT?

FIRST--AND I CAN'T BELIEVE I EVEN HAVE TO *SAY* THIS--THERE'S OBVIOUSLY NO POSSIBILITY OF SHARIA TAKING ROOT IN AMERICA. THIS IS JUST THE LATEST RIGHT WING ATTEMPT TO STRIKE *FEAR* INTO THE HEARTS OF *SIMPLETONS.*

SECOND--IF THERE *WERE* ANY SUPPORT FOR THE IMPOSITION OF AN AUTHORITARIAN PATRIARCHAL HOMOPHOBIC FUNDAMENTALIST LEGAL SYSTEM IN THE U.S.--

--WOULDN'T IT BE FROM THE *RIGHT?*

GASP! MOONBAT, DID I *HEAR* YOU CORRECTLY?

DID YOU JUST COMPARE CONSERVATIVES TO *ISLAMOFASCISTS?* HAVE YOU NO *SHAME?* IS THERE NO DEPTH TO WHICH YOU WILL NOT *SINK?*

BUT-- BUT *YOU* JUST--

QUIET, M.B! I'M WORKING ON MY *NEW* CASE-- THE MYSTERY OF THE *DEGENERATE LEFT!*

YOU KNOW WHO *ELSE* EMPLOYED HYPERBOLE AS A RHETORICAL DEVICE? *HITLER!!*

ER--I-- WHAT?

this modern world
by tom tomorrow

Panel 1:
AH, MOONBAT! COME IN! HOW DO YOU LIKE MY "TREEHOUSE OF **LOVE**"?

OH DEAR GOD, DO I EVEN **WANT** TO KNOW WHAT'S GOING ON HERE?

Panel 2:
A FEMALE TV REPORTER SAYS SHE WANTS TO **INTERVIEW** ME, MOONBAT--BUT I'M NOT FOOLED! WHAT SHE **REALLY** WANTS IS TO MAKE CONSERVATIVE CITIZEN JOURNALISTS SUCH AS MYSELF LOOK **CRAZY** AND **UNPROFESSIONAL**!

Panel 3:
SO I'M GOING TO TURN THE TABLES ON **HER**--BY TRANSFORMING MY TREEHOUSE HEADQUARTERS INTO A METICULOUSLY-PREPARED DEN OF **SEDUCTION**!

WOULD YOU CARE FOR A LITTLE BUBBLY? BY WHICH I MEAN 7-UP.

UH, NO. THANK YOU.

Panel 4:
THE EXOTIC LIGHTING AND MOOD MUSIC **MAY** CAUSE HER TO FALL UNDER MY ROMANTIC **SPELL**...OR PERHAPS SHE'LL SIMPLY BECOME FLUSTERED AND SAY SOMETHING FOOLISH! IN EITHER CASE, IT SHOULD MAKE FOR SOME COMPELLING **CITIZEN JOURNALISM**, EXPOSING THE HYPOCRISY OF THE MAINSTREAM MEDIA!

Panel 5:

Panel 6:
AND YOU'RE DOING THIS TO DEMONSTRATE HOW **NOT** CRAZY YOU ARE.

OBVIOUSLY! SAY, CAN YOU HELP ME HIDE THIS WEBCAM IN MY **PANTS**?

UH--I HAVE TO GO NOW. I JUST REMEMBERED A PHONE CALL I NEED TO MAKE.

NEXT: BY MOONBAT **BETRAYED**!

THIS MODERN WORLD

by TOM TOMORROW

THE NEWS FROM SIX MONTHS FROM NOW

IN SOME PARALLEL UNIVERSE

AND MAYBE HERE AS WELL

1) TEA PARTY IDEOLOGUES FIGHT TO ENACT THEIR **UNIQUE** BRAND OF POPULISM!

WE INTEND TO CUT **TAXES** FOR THE **RICH**--AND TO CUT THE **MINIMUM WAGE, UNEMPLOYMENT BENEFITS** AND **SOCIAL SECURITY** FOR EVERYONE **ELSE!**

THAT WAY **EVERYBODY** GETS A CUT!

IT'S ONLY **FAIR!**

2) THEY ALSO TAKE A COURAGEOUS STAND AGAINST THE TERRIFYING MENACE OF **MODEST HEALTH CARE REFORM!**

WE WILL SHUT DOWN THE **GOVERNMENT** IF NECESSARY!

ALTERNATELY WE MIGHT HOLD OUR COLLECTIVE BREATH UNTIL WE TURN **BLUE!**

FORTUNATELY, **WE** HAVE HEALTH CARE.

3) MEANWHILE, CHRISTINE O'DONNELL'S SURPRISE VICTORY* LEADS TO RISE OF STRIDENT SELF-GRATIFICATION LOBBY.

WHEN MASTURBATION IS OUTLAWED-- ONLY **OUTLAWS** WILL MASTURBATE!

YOU'LL PRY **MY** PRIVATE PARTS FROM MY **COLD DEAD FINGERS!**

NATIONAL MASTURBATION ASSOCIATION

*POSSIBLY DUE TO INTERVENTION OF UNSPEAKABLE OCCULT FORCES.

4) REPUBLICANS REACT TO **SUBPOENA POWER** WITH ALL THE SELF-RESTRAINT OF JUNKIES ON AN OXYCONTIN BINGE.

THE SUBCOMMITTEE ON OBAMA'S KENYAN BIRTH CERTIFICATE AND ALSO HE'S A MARXIST WILL NOW COME TO **ORDER!**

WE WELCOME OUR FIRST EXPERT WITNESS--**GLENN BECK!**

SOB!

5) AND OF COURSE, THE ADMINISTRATION CONTINUES TO BLAME ITS TROUBLES ON **LEFT-WING BLOGGERS.**

EVERYTHING WOULD HAVE BEEN **FINE**--IF IT WEREN'T FOR THOSE **DARNED MEDDLING KIDS!**

RUH ROH!

TOM TOMORROW © 2010...www.thismodernworld.com...twitter.com/tomtomorrow

THIS MODERN WORLD

by TOM TOMORROW

Panel 1:

INVISIBLE-HAND-OF-THE-FREE-MARKET MAN HAS CORNERED A FOUL *MISCREANT!*

I AM HERE TO DEFEND THE PROPERTY RIGHTS OF WHATEVER INDETERMINATE FINANCIAL ENTITY MOMENTARILY CONTROLS YOUR SECURITIZED *MORTGAGE--*

--BY FORECLOSING YOUR *HOME!*

?

Panel 2:

BUT--THERE'S BEEN A MISTAKE! I DON'T EVEN *HAVE* A MORTGAGE!

THAT'S NOT WHAT THEY TOLD ME AT FAT EDDIE'S PAWN SHOP AND FORECLOSURE MILL! NOW START *PACKING*, DEADBEAT!

Panel 3:

HOLD IT RIGHT THERE!

WHO THE HELL ARE *YOU*?

I AM THE *REGULATOR*--AND THESE DOCUMENTS OUTLINE THE FRAUD AND ABUSE ENDEMIC IN THE FORECLOSURE INDUSTRY!

I'M SHUTTING YOU *DOWN*, HAND!

Panel 4:

EH, WHATEVER. YOU MAY WIN THIS ROUND--BUT IN THE LONG RUN, YOU DON'T STAND A *CHANCE* AGAINST *ME!*

HOW DO YOU FIGURE?

ALLOW ME TO DEMONSTRATE.

Panel 5:

CITIZEN--WOULD YOU RATHER PUT YOUR FAITH IN THE UNFETTERED *FREE MARKET*--OR IN MISTER *INTRUSIVE GOVERNMENT REGULATION* HERE?

OH, *DEFINITELY* THE FREE MARKET. NO QUESTION!

WHAT?!

Panel 6:

BUT--BUT I JUST SAVED YOUR *HOME!*

OH, YEAH. AND, HEY, THANKS FOR THAT. STILL, CAN'T HAVE BIG GOVERNMENT RUNNING OUR LIVES, YOU KNOW?

MY WORK HERE IS CLEARLY DONE!

FOR NOW.

Panel 7:

SOON

I'M BACK.

REGULATOR! *HELP!* I CHANGED MY *MIND!*

TOM TOMORROW ©2010....www.thismodernworld.com....twitter.com/tomtomorrow

10

THIS MODERN WORLD

BY TOM TOMORROW

Panel 1:
READY TO SEE THIS YEAR'S TER-RIFYING HALLOWEEN COSTUME?

I CAN BARELY CON-TAIN MY EXCITEMENT.

Panel 2:
TA-DAAAA!

UH--YOU'RE GOING AS...ME?

EXACTLY!

Panel 3:
I'M A RIGHT-WING TEA PARTIER WHO THINKS THAT *CHRISTINE O'DONNELL* AND *CARL PALADINO*-- NOT TO MENTION JOE MILLER AND SHARRON ANGLE AND THAT GUY WHO LIKES TO DRESS UP LIKE A *NAZI*--ARE THE FINEST POLITICIANS THIS COUNTRY HAS TO *OFFER!*

Panel 4:
I THINK THAT BARACK OBAMA IS PROBABLY A *KENYAN MUSLIM SOCIALIST* WITH A GENETIC PRE-DISPOSITION TOWARD *ANTI-COL-ONIALISM!* AND GLENN BECK IS A COURAGEOUS TRUTH-TELLER WHO HAS UNCOVERED A CENTURY-LONG PROGRESSIVE CONSPIRACY TO *DESTROY AMERICA!*

Panel 5:
BASICALLY, I'M SO DELUSIONAL, IT'S A WONDER THAT I'M ABLE TO PERFORM SIMPLE DAILY TASKS-- AND THERE ARE *MILLIONS* JUST *LIKE* ME! AND THE *TRULY* TERRIFYING THING IS--

--WE *VOTE!!*

BWAH HA HA HA HA!

Panel 6:
SIGH...AND DO I EVEN WANT TO *ASK* ABOUT THE DOG?

OH, HE'S THE *GHOST* OF A CHANCE...THAT WE'LL *EVER* HAVE A SANE POLITICAL PROCESS IN THIS COUNTRY!

NO, I AM NOT. I'M JUST A GHOST.

BOO.

CAN WE GO NOW?

Tom Tomorrow © 2010 ... www.thismodernworld.com ...twitter.com/tomtomorrow

THIS MODERN WORLD

by TOM TOMORROW

Panel 1: THE BANKING INDUSTRY UNVEILS AN INNOVATIVE NEW FINANCIAL INSTRUMENT.

THANKS TO A PREVIOUSLY UN-NOTICED REGULATORY LOOPHOLE, WE CAN NOW OFFER *CASH ADVANCES* BASED ON THE ESTIMATED LIFETIME EARNINGS OF YOUR *OFFSPRING!*

IN OTHER WORDS, YOU CAN *LITERALLY* MORTGAGE YOUR CHILDREN'S FUTURE!

Panel 2: CASH-STRAPPED AMERICANS EAGERLY EMBRACE THE OPPORTUNITY.

I MORTGAGED *MY* KIDS' FUTURE SO I COULD REMODEL THE DOWNSTAIRS *BATHROOM!*

I WENT TO CLUB MED--*AND* BOUGHT A 52-INCH FLAT-SCREEN!

IT'S LIKE 2005 AGAIN-- ONLY *BETTER!*

Panel 3: BUT LENDING STANDARDS SOON GROW LAX.

WE'D LIKE TO MORTGAGE THE FUTURE OF CHILDREN WE DO NOT YET ACTUALLY *HAVE!*

AND *I'D* LIKE TO MAKE THAT LOAN--AND THEN IMMEDIATELY DUMP IT ON WALL STREET AT A *PROFIT!*

SO HOW MUCH DO YOU WANT?

SKY'S THE LIMIT.

REALLY.

Panel 4: INEVITABLY THE BUBBLE BURSTS.

KIDS, I HAVE SOME BAD NEWS. THE MORTGAGE THAT WE TOOK OUT ON YOUR FUTURE EXCEEDS ANY AMOUNT YOU CAN POSSIBLY EVER HOPE TO EARN.

IN SHORT, YOU'RE UNDERWATER.

SORRY 'BOUT THAT!

Panel 5: AND THEN THINGS GET *REALLY* COMPLICATED.

I'M HERE TO FORECLOSE YOUR CHILDREN AND PUT THEM TO WORK IN A FACTORY SOMEWHERE.

WAIT! HIS PAPERWORK WAS IMPROPERLY FILED! *I* HOLD THE LIEN ON THOSE KIDS!

Panel 6: BUT NOT TO WORRY--THE *BANKERS* QUICKLY RECOVER!

WE WERE VICTIMIZED BY *PREDATORY BORROWERS*--BUT THE WISDOM OF THE FREE MARKET *PREVAILED!*

WHICH IS TO SAY, WE GOT ANOTHER TAXPAYER BAILOUT.

WHO COULD HAVE FORESEEN IT?

N E X T: THANKS TO OUR NEW PARTNERSHIP WITH *SATAN*-- --YOU CAN NOW MORTGAGE YOUR VERY *SOUL!*

THIS MODERN WORLD

by TOM TOMORROW

VOTERS LARGELY SHUN THE PARTY UNABLE TO FIX THE ECONOMIC MESS IN FAVOR OF THE PARTY THAT *CAUSED* IT.

ER--ARE YOU REFERRING TO SOMETHING THAT HAPPENED BEFORE JANUARY OF 2009?

I HAVE LITTLE RECOLLECTION OF THAT DISTANT ERA.

ON THE LEFT, AN OLD DEBATE RAGES ANEW.

DEMOCRATS WOULD HAVE DONE--

--BETTER!-- --WORSE!--

--IF WE'D BEEN MORE PROGRESSIVE!

(WE'LL NEVER KNOW EITHER WAY NOW.)

SOME PEOPLE ACTUALLY SEEM TO BELIEVE THAT LEFT-WING *BLOGGERS* ARE RESPONSIBLE FOR THE DEMOCRATS' LOSSES.

THEY *CRITICIZED* THE PRESIDENT-- AND *LOOK WHAT HAPPENED!*

IF ONLY THEY WOULD USE THEIR INCOMPREHENSIBLE POWER FOR *GOOD* AND NOT *EVIL!*

THE PUNDITOCRACY BLAMES LIBERALISM ITSELF.

OBAMA WAS INSUFFICIENTLY *CONTEMPTUOUS* OF HIS BASE!

TO SUCCEED *NOW*, HE MUST TREAT THEM WITH THE RESPECT ONE MIGHT ACCORD A *PEDERAST!*

OR A SERIAL KILLER.

G.O.P. LEADERS QUICKLY DECLARE A MANDATE--

--TO EXTEND BUSH'S TAX CUTS FOR THE EXCEEDINGLY WEALTHY!

THE AMERICAN PEOPLE HAVE *SPOKEN!*

WE ARE BUT THEIR HUMBLE *SERVANTS!*

OBAMA INSISTS THAT DEMOCRATS AND REPUBLICANS CAN STILL FIND COMMON GROUND.

FOR INSTANCE, I THINK WE CAN *ALL* AGREE THAT *PUPPIES* ARE *ADORABLE!*

I BEG TO DIFFER.

TEA PARTIERS *ARE* OPEN TO COMPROMISE, AS LONG AS THEY GET EXACTLY WHAT THEY WANT.

NICE LITTLE BICAMERAL LEGISLATIVE BODY YOU GOT HERE.

BE A SHAME IF ANYTHING *HAPPENED* TO IT.

MEANWHILE AN OLD DEBATE ALSO RAGES ON THE *RIGHT*.

REPUBLICANS WOULD HAVE DONE--

--BETTER!-- --WORSE!--

--IF WE'D BEEN MORE *RE*GRESSIVE!

NUT-JOB.

SELL-OUT.

ALL IN ALL, AN ERA OF POLITE BIPARTISANSHIP IS PROBABLY NOT IN THE CARDS.

BUT IF WE CONTINUALLY DEMONIZE OUR FRIENDS ACROSS THE AISLE-- HOW CAN WE EVER "WORK TOGETHER" TO "GET THINGS DONE"?

EXCELLENT POINT, SOCIALIST SCUMBAG.

THIS MODERN WORLD

by TOM TOMORROW

AS EXPECTED, THE CO-CHAIRS OF OBAMA'S BIPARTISAN DEFICIT COMMISSION JUST CAME OUT IN FAVOR OF RAISING THE SOCIAL SECURITY RETIREMENT AGE.

HOLY **CAT-FOOD!**

MANY PEOPLE THINK IT'S A PERFECTLY SENSIBLE THING TO DO-- BECAUSE STATISTICALLY, AMERICANS **LIVE** LONGER THAN THEY USED TO!

OF COURSE, STATISTICS CAN BE **MISLEADING.**

WHILE LIFE EXPECTANCY FOR A 65-YEAR-OLD MALE IN THE TOP HALF OF INCOME EARNERS **HAS** INCREASED BY SIX YEARS OVER THE PAST THREE DECADES--

--THE COMPARABLE INCREASE FOR THOSE IN THE **BOTTOM** HALF WAS BARELY MORE THAN A **YEAR!*

*ACCORDING TO SOCIAL SECURITY ADMINISTRATION DATA.

SO IN OTHER WORDS, THE WHOLE "LIFESPAN" ARGUMENT IS REALLY LITTLE MORE THAN A CRUEL **JOKE.**

AS PAUL KRUGMAN SAYS, WE'D BE TELLING **JANITORS** THEY CAN'T RETIRE--

--BECAUSE **LAWYERS** ARE LIVING LONGER.

ULTIMATELY, IT'S A QUESTION OF **PRIORITIES.** IF WE BELIEVE IN EXTENDING TAX CUTS TO THE WEALTHY WHILE FORCING LOW-INCOME SENIORS TO WORK 'TIL THEY **DROP**--

--THEN WE PROBABLY NEED TO ASK OURSELVES--

--WHAT KIND OF MONSTERS **ARE** WE?

UM--OKAY--SO WHAT THE HELL WAS **THAT** ALL ABOUT?

HEY--YOU THINK IT'S EASY MAKING THIS STUFF ENTERTAINING, **YOU** GIVE IT A TRY.

TOM TOMORROW ©2010····www.thismodernworld.com····twitter.com/tomtomorrow

14

THIS MODERN WORLD

by TOM TOMORROW

Panel 1:
JUST IN TIME FOR THE HOLIDAYS... THE LASTEST INCARNATION OF--

Security Theatre Follies

WE'LL MAKE YOU FEEL **SAFER**--

--BY FEELING YOU **UP**!

Panel 2:
AIRPORT SECURITY WAS ALREADY AN ELABORATE KABUKI RITUAL OF POINTLESS ACTIVITY.

I FLY WITH CONFIDENCE, KNOWING THAT CARRY-ON TOILETRIES ARE LIMITED TO MULTIPLE **SMALL** BOTTLES RATHER THAN A SINGLE **LARGE** BOTTLE!

YOU'D HAVE TO BE SOME KIND OF TERRORIST **MASTERMIND** TO FIGURE OUT A WAY AROUND **THAT**!

Panel 3:
NOW IT'S BEING TAKEN TO AN ENTIRELY NEW LEVEL.

YOU CAN SUBMIT TO AN INVASIVE, HUMILIATING **FULL BODY SCAN**--OR AN INVASIVE, HUMILIATING **FULL BODY PATDOWN**!

IN OTHER WORDS, YOU CAN EITHER BE **OGLED**--OR **GROPED**!

OR BE FINED $11,000 IF YOU MAKE A FUSS ABOUT IT.

Panel 4:
ACCORDING TO ONE POLL, 81% OF AMERICANS SUPPORT THE NEW PROCEDURES.

AS LONG AS YOU UNQUESTIONINGLY ACCEPT T.S.A ASSURANCES CONCERNING HEALTH AND PRIVACY ISSUES--AND/OR DON'T MIND BEING INTIMATELY FONDLED BY STRANGERS--

--AND/OR DON'T MIND WATCHING STRANGERS FONDLE YOUR **CHILDREN**--

--WHAT POSSIBLE OBJECTION COULD YOU **HAVE**?

Panel 5:
AT THIS POINT, WE'RE PROBABLY ONE TERRORISM SCARE AWAY FROM ROUTINE FULL-BODY CAVITY SEARCHES.

NO PROBLEM! *I* HAVE NOTHING TO HIDE!

Panel 6:
MAYBE IT'S ALL SOME KIND OF **TEST**.

JUDGING FROM OUR ONGOING RESEARCH, THE HUMANS ARE **LAUGHABLY** SUBSERVIENT TO PERCEIVED AUTHORITY!

THIS WILL BE THE EASIEST PLANET WE'VE EVER **ENSLAVED**!

TOM TOMORROW ©2010 ...www.thismodernworld.com...twitter.com/tomtomorrow

THIS MODERN WORLD

by TOM TOMORROW

THE NEW BIPARTI-SANSHIP

—*featuring*—

The Tepid Moderate *and* The Right-Wing Nutjob

"Two sides of the same coin"

CLEARLY WE DON'T SEE EYE TO EYE ON EVERYTHING--BUT THERE MUST BE *SOMETHING* DEMOCRATS AND REPUBLICANS CAN WORK TOGETHER TO ACHIEVE!

YES--THE DEMISE OF THE DEMOCRAT PARTY!

ER-- WHAT?

LOOK--JUST SINCE THE ELECTION, REPUBLICAN LEADERS HAVE SNUBBED A PRESIDENTIAL INVITATION, ANNOUNCED THAT THEIR ONLY GOAL FOR THE NEXT TWO YEARS IS TO DEFEAT OBAMA, *AND* ARE EVEN BLOCKING A NUCLEAR ARMS TREATY!

DO WE HAVE TO HIRE A SKYWRITER AND SPELL IT OUT IN GIANT LETTERS FOR YOU?

WE'RE NOT *INTERESTED* IN FINDING COMMON GROUND! WE'RE INTERESTED IN SCORCHED EARTH, TAKE-NO-PRISONERS *ANNIHILATION!* WE *DESPISE* YOU WITH THE RAGING INTENSITY OF A THOUSAND WHITE HOT SUNS! IF YOU REACH ACROSS THE AISLE WE WILL CHOP OFF YOUR ARM WITH A *HATCHET!*

OKAY, WE HAVE SOME PHILISOPHICAL DIFFERENCES. BUT *SURELY* WE CAN FIND A WAY TO--

DIE, LIBERAL SCUM! *DIE!*

TOM TOMORROW ©2010·····www.thismodernworld.com···.twitter.com/tomtomorrow

16

THIS MODERN WORLD

by TOM TOMORROW

Panel 1:
IT'S THAT GREAT AMERICAN CHAMPION OF MODERATION, BIPARTISANSHIP, AND *FURTHER* MODERATION...

MIDDLE MAN

WE MUST SET ASIDE OUR DIFFERENCES--AND GET THINGS *DONE!*

WHATEVER THEY ARE.

JUST, YOU KNOW-- *THINGS.*

Panel 2:
AFTER A BRUISING DEFEAT AT THE HANDS OF HIS ESTEEMED ARCH-RIVALS, *MISTER ORANGE* AND THE *HUMAN TURTLE*, MIDDLE-MAN STRIKES BACK--WITH THE AWESOME POWER OF *CIVILITY!*

PLEASE ACCEPT MY *APOLOGIES!* I HAVE BEEN REGRETTABLY INATTENTIVE TO *YOUR* PRIORITIES!

NOW WE'RE GETTING SOMEWHERE!

Panel 3:
BUT AS SOON AS HE TURNS HIS *BACK*...

WE HAD A *VERY* PRODUCTIVE MEETING WITH MIDDLE-MAN!

AND NOW WE INTEND TO DESTROY HIM, AS PLANNED.

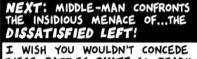

Panel 4:
LATER, AT HIS SECRET HIDEOUT...

I CAN'T BELIEVE THEY WOULD *DO* THIS! I THOUGHT WE HAD AN *UNDERSTANDING!*

CLEARLY THE FAULT MUST BE *MINE!*

THERE'S ONLY ONE THING LEFT TO DO *NOW!*

Panel 5:
SHORTLY THEREAFTER...

AND SO I WILL *FORCE* YOU TO COMPROMISE--BY GIVING YOU *EXACTLY WHAT YOU WANT!*

CURSES! MIDDLE-MAN HAS FOILED US *AGAIN!*

HOW CAN WE *BEAR* THE IGNOMINY?

AND CIVILITY TRIUMPHS ONCE *MORE!*

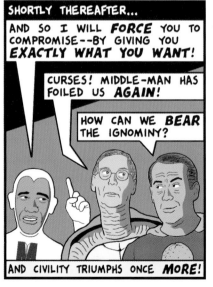

Panel 6:
NEXT: MIDDLE-MAN CONFRONTS THE INSIDIOUS MENACE OF...THE *DISSATISFIED LEFT!*

I WISH YOU WOULDN'T CONCEDE THESE BATTLES *QUITE* SO READILY, MIDDLE-MAN.

STOP *WHINING*, DAMN YOU! I'LL *NEVER* COMPROMISE--

--WITH *YOU!!*

TOM TOMORROW © 2010...www.thismodernworld.com...twitter.com/tomtomorrow

THIS MODERN WORLD

by TOM TOMORROW

Panel 1:

HEY THERE, BIFF! HAPPY HOLIDAYS!

DON'T YOU MEAN "MERRY CHRISTMAS"? OR ARE YOU JUST ANOTHER FOOTSOLDIER IN GEORGE SOROS' GRAND SCHEME TO **DESTROY CHRISTMAS**?

WELL, AREN'T **WE** JUST BRIMMING WITH HOLIDAY SPIRIT! BEEN WATCHING FOX NEWS AGAIN, HAVE YOU?

Panel 2:

LOOK--GENERIC HOLIDAY GREETINGS ARE A GESTURE OF BASIC INCLUSIVENESS. I DON'T KNOW IF YOU'VE HEARD ABOUT THIS, BUT OUR **JEWISH** FRIENDS--FOR EXAMPLE--DO NOT TRADITIONALLY CELEBRATE THE BIRTH OF THE CHRISTIAN MESSIAH.

Panel 3:

BUT MAYBE MORE TO THE POINT-- THERE ARE **TWO** MAJOR HOLIDAYS COMING UP--CHRISTMAS **AND** NEW YEAR'S! GET IT? HOLIDAYS--**PLURAL**!

I MEAN, IT'S **POSSIBLE** THAT ANYONE WHO SAYS "HAPPY HOLIDAYS" OR "SEASON'S GREETINGS" IS PART OF A VAST CONSPIRACY TO UNDERMINE CHRISTIANITY ITSELF--

Panel 4:

--BUT MAYBE THEY'RE JUST TRYING TO WISH YOU A HAPPY HOLIDAY SEASON.

Panel 5:

Panel 6:

YOU KNOW, THAT ACTUALLY MAKES A LOT OF SENSE.

MY GOD, IT'S A FESTIVUS **MIRACLE**!

UNLESS IT'S WHAT GEORGE SOROS **WANTS** US TO THINK.

I **KNEW** IT COULDN'T LAST.

TOM TOMORROW © 2010····www.thismodernworld.com····twitter.com/tomtomorrow

THIS MODERN WORLD

by TOM TOMORROW

The Very Wealthy Man

an innocent fable, of no relevance to contemporary events

ONE DAY, A VERY WEALTHY MAN TOOK A VERY BIG RISK.

THESE NIGERIAN-EMAIL-BACKED SECURITIES LOOK LIKE A **FANTASTIC** INVESTMENT!

GET MY **BROKER** ON THE LINE!

SADLY, THINGS DID NOT TURN OUT WELL.

THE NIGERIAN-EMAIL-BACKED DERIVATIVES MARKET HAS **COLLAPSED**!

NO ONE COULD HAVE FORESEEN IT!

Action McNews Network

SERIOUS PEOPLE AGREED--SOMETHING HAD TO BE DONE!

IT WOULD BE DISASTROUS FOR US **ALL** IF THE VERY WEALTHY MAN WERE FORCED TO SUFFER THE CONSEQUENCES OF HIS ACTIONS!

HE IS **TOO RICH** TO **FAIL**!

SO EVERYONE PITCHED IN!

TO PAY FOR THE BAILOUT, OUR TOWN IS ELIMINATING THE **POLICE** AND **FIRE** DEPARTMENTS!

I GUESS WE'VE **ALL** GOT TO TIGHTEN OUR BELTS!

EXCEPT FOR THE VERY WEALTHY MAN!

OBVIOUSLY.

AND THE VERY WEALTHY MAN LIVED HAPPILY EVER AFTER.

THESE HERBAL-MALE-ENHANCEMENT-BACKED SECURITIES LOOK LIKE A **FANTASTIC** INVESTMENT!

GET MY **BROKER** ON THE LINE!

TOM TOMORROW © 2011 ... www.thismodernworld.com ... twitter.com/tomtomorrow

THIS MODERN WORLD

by TOM TOMORROW

 **2010** AN INCOMPLETE AND SUBJECTIVE LOOK AT **THE YEAR IN CRAZY** PART THE FIRST

JAN. 14: UNHAPPY WITH DEMOCRATS, SHARRON ANGLE SUGGESTS "2ND AMENDMENT REMEDIES" MIGHT BE NEEDED.

YOU'LL PRY **MY** RIGHT TO BE REFUSED HEALTH CARE FROM MY COLD DEAD FINGERS!

JAN. 21: SUPREME COURT HANDS DEMOCRACY OVER TO HIGHEST BIDDER.

IF CORPORATIONS ARE NOT FREE TO MAKE UNLIMITED ANONYMOUS CAMPAIGN CONTRIBUTIONS--

--THEN **NONE** OF US ARE TRULY FREE!

JAN. 25: JAMES O'KEEFE ARRESTED TRYING TO WIRE-TAP A SENATOR'S OFFICE.

WHAT PART OF "CITIZEN JOURNALISM" DON'T YOU **UNDERSTAND?**

FEB. 16: DICK CHENEY CONFESSES:

"I WAS A **BIG SUPPORTER** OF WATER-BOARDING!"

INEXPLICABLY, NO PROSECUTION ENSUES.

FEB. 25: NOT-AT-ALL CRAZY RIGHT-WINGERS SAY MISSILE DEFENSE LOGO PROVES OBAMA'S SUBMISSION TO SHARIA.

HE IS UNDERMINING AMERICA THROUGH **GRAPHIC DESIGN!**

MAR. 21: CONGRESS PASSES MODEST HEALTH CARE REFORM; CONSERVATIVE MELTDOWN ENSUES.

SOCIALISM! | DEATH PANELS!

YARGLE BARGLE **BLARGH!**

APRIL 7: OBAMA AUTHORIZES ASSASSINATION OF AMERICAN CITIZEN ACCUSED OF TERRORISM.

EXECUTIVE OVERREACH IS **OKAY** IF YOU'RE A **DEMOCRAT!**

APRIL 14: NOT-AT-ALL CRAZY RIGHT-WINGERS FIND ANOTHER ADMINISTRATION LOGO WITH HIDDEN MUSLIM SYMBOLS!

WHERE WILL THIS GRAPHIC SUBVERSION **END?**

Nuclear Security Summit

APRIL 15: TEA PARTIERS ACROSS COUNTRY GATHER TO DENOUNCE THEIR TAX BURDEN--

--WHICH, FOR MOST, WENT **DOWN** UNDER OBAMA.

WHUT?

APRIL 20: NOT-AT-ALL RACIST ARIZONA HOUSE VOTES FOR PROVISION REQUIRING OBAMA TO SHOW BIRTH CERTIFICATE BEFORE 2012 ELECTION.

WE JUST WANT TO BE SURE HE'S NOT **CANADIAN!**

MAY 14: IN WAKE OF B.P. OIL SPILL, HALEY BARBOUR ENCOURAGES TOURISTS TO "ENJOY THE BEACH"!

IT'S PRACTICALLY **PRISTINE**, IF YOU IGNORE THE TARBALLS & ALL THE DEAD FISH!

MAY 21: ADMINISTRATION WINS RIGHT TO DETAIN PEOPLE WITHOUT HABEAS.

WHAT COULD **POSSIBLY** GO WRONG? | BEATS **ME!**

JUNE 6: RUSH LIMBAUGH TRADITIONALLY MARRIES FOR FOURTH TIME.

THANK GOODNESS THIS SACRED INSTITUTION HAS NOT BEEN SULLIED BY VILE **HOMOSEXUALS!**

SUCH AS MY WEDDING SINGER, ELTON JOHN.

JUNE 17: REP. BARTON APOLOGIZES TO B.P.

I DON'T KNOW **HOW** OUR OCEAN GOT IN THE WAY OF YOUR OIL!

CAN YOU **EVER** FORGIVE US?

JUNE 18: MICHELE BACHMAN REFUSES TO FILL OUT CONSTITUTIONALLY-MANDATED CENSUS.

IT'S A SOCIALIST **PLOT**--TO FIND OUT HOW MANY TOILETS I HAVE!

NEXT: **MORE** CRAZY!

TOM TOMORROW© 2010... www.thismodernworld.com

20

THIS MODERN WORLD

by TOM TOMORROW

2010
AN INCOMPLETE AND SUBJECTIVE LOOK AT **THE YEAR IN CRAZY**
PART THE SECOND

JUNE 19: GLENN BECK FAN OPENS FIRE ON COPS; WAS ON WAY TO MASSACRE EMPLOYEES AT BECK-DEMONIZED *TIDES* FOUNDATION.

LATER IN THE YEAR, THE SHOOTER WILL OPENLY ACKNOWLEDGE THAT HIS PLAN WAS INSPIRED BY THINGS BECK "EXPOSED."

JULY 20: BREITBART/ SHERROD FIASCO BEGINS.

IF A RIGHT WING PROVOC-ATEUR SAYS "JUMP"--

--OUR ONLY QUESTION IS, "WOULD YOU LIKE US TO FIRE SOMEONE FIRST?"

JULY 27: DEPARTMENT OF DEFENSE SAYS 96% OF IRAQ RECONSTRUCTION MONEY UNACCOUNTED FOR.

BUT HEY-- WHAT'S 8.7 BILLION DOL-LARS BETWEEN FRIENDS?

MONTH OF AUGUST: CONS FREAK OUT OVER "GROUND ZERO MOSQUE."

IF WE ALLOW THE SACRED GROUND OF A FORMER BURLINGTON COAT FACTORY TO BE DESECRATED--

--THE TER-RORISTS HAVE **WON!**

AUG. 28: PUDGY WHITE CONSPIRACY THEORIST LAYS CLAIM TO THE MANTLE OF REV. MARTIN LUTHER KING.

IF MLK WERE ALIVE TODAY, HE'D BE OB-SESSED WITH GEORGE SOROS **TOO!**

SEPT. 8: OBAMA D.O.J. WINS COURT RULING SHIELDING TORTURE AND RENDITION AS "STATE SECRETS."

I **PROMISE** TO BE OUT-RAGED WHEN THIS PRECEDENT IS ABUSED BY REPUBLICANS!

SEPT. 19: B.P. FINALLY SEALS WELL; EVERYONE POLITELY AGREES TO PRE-TEND MASSIVE AMOUNTS OF OIL HAVE MAGICALLY DISAPPEARED.

OIL'S WELL THAT **ENDS** WELL!

HEH HEH!

SEPT. 23: BANK FORE-CLOSES HOUSE OF FLORIDA MAN WHO DID NOT EVEN HAVE A MORTGAGE.

THAT'S NOT WHAT IT SAYS ON **OUR** PAPERWORK--

--LEGALLY NOTARIZED BY "HEYWOOD JABLOWME!"

NOV. 2: G.O.P. TAKES HOUSE. ALSO, OKLAHOMANS VOTE TO PROTECT SELVES FROM DIRE THREAT OF **SHARIA LAW!**

WE'RE PASSING AN ANTI-**VOLDEMORT** MEASURE NEXT!

JUST TO BE SAFE.

NOV. 3: GEORGE BUSH CONFESSES:

DAMN **RIGHT** I AUTH-ORIZED WATERBOARDING!

INEXPLICABLY, NO PROSE-CUTION ENSUES.

NOV. 16: NEWLY-ELECTED ANTI-HEALTH-CARE CON-GRESSMAN WANTS TO KNOW WHY HE HAS TO WAIT A MONTH FOR HEALTH CARE.

THERE OUGHTA BE A **LAW!**

DEC. 6: OBAMA CAVES ON TAX CUTS; PROMISES TO **REALLY** FIGHT IN TWO YEARS.

IF BY "FIGHT" YOU MEAN "PRE-EMPTIVELY CONCEDE ONCE AGAIN."

WHICH I DO.

DEC. 6: FOX NEWS DEM-OCRAT BOB BECKEL URGES U.S. GOV'T TO ASSASSINATE JULIAN ASSANGE.

WHAT OTHER APPROPRIATE RESPONSE **IS** THERE--

--TO A GUY WITH A **WEB-SITE**??

MONTH OF DECEMBER: FOX'S ANNUAL WAR ON IMAGINARY WAR ON CHRIST-MAS BEGINS YET AGAIN!

DON'T YOU JUST **LOVE** THE OLD FAMILIAR TRADITIONS?

NOT TO MENTION...

Texas school board rewriting history; Ginni Thomas asking Anita Hill for apology; every-thing Christine O'Donnell said; Chertoff airport scanner conflict of interest; 1/3 of Republicans who believe Obama is a Mus-lim; ABC/Breitbart fias-co; Boehner campaign-ing for Nazi re-enactor guy; etc., etc., etc...

SEE YOU **NEXT** YEAR!

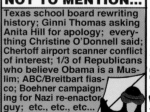

TOM TOMORROW© 2010... www.thismodernworld.com

THIS MODERN WORLD

by TOM TOMORROW

SO I SUPPOSE YOU'RE GOING TO TRY TO **EXPLOIT** THE INCIDENT IN TUCSON TO SCORE SOME CHEAP POLITICAL POINT ABOUT **GUNS**?

"INCIDENT"? YOU MEAN THE ASSASSINATION ATTEMPT WHICH LEFT SIX PEOPLE DEAD, INCLUDING A NINE-YEAR-OLD CHILD?

THERE YOU GO, WITH YOUR **INCENDIARY RHETORIC!** YOU KNOW PERFECTLY WELL THAT IF THE KILLER HADN'T HAD A **GUN**--

--YES, YES, I KNOW-- HE WOULD HAVE KILLED THOSE PEOPLE WITH SOMETHING ELSE. LAWN FURNITURE, MAYBE.

LOOK, WE HAVE THIS SAME CONVERSATION AFTER EVERY GUN MASSACRE. I'M NOT GOING TO CHANGE YOUR MIND, AND YOU'RE NOT GOING TO CHANGE MINE.

BUT RELAX! YOUR PARANOID POLITICAL FANTASIES NOTWITHSTANDING, NO ONE'S GOING TO TAKE YOUR GUNS AWAY!

BARRING SOME SEISMIC REALIGNMENT IN THIS COUNTRY, THE GUN CONTROL DEBATE IS ALL BUT SETTLED--AND YOUR SIDE WON. THE OCCASIONAL HORRIFIC CIVILIAN MASSACRE IS JUST THE PRICE THE REST OF US HAVE TO PAY.

OVER AND OVER AGAIN, APPARENTLY.

I'M EXTREMELY OFFENDED BY THE WAY YOU PHRASED THAT.

OF COURSE YOU ARE, YOU DELICATE FLOWER, YOU.

THIS MODERN WORLD

by TOM TOMORROW

Panel 1: THE SHOOTINGS IN ARIZONA WERE AN *ISOLATED INCIDENT!* THERE ARE *NO LARGER CONCLUSIONS* TO BE DRAWN!

IT'S TRUE THAT LOUGHNER'S MOTIVATIONS REMAIN UNCLEAR--

Panel 2: --BUT WHAT ABOUT THE GUY ARRESTED FOR THREATENING SEN. PATTY MURRAY'S LIFE?

ISOLATED.

THE GUY ARRESTED FOR THREATENING MURRAY'S SUPPORTERS-- WITH A *CLEAVER?*

ISOLATED.

Panel 3: THE GUY ARRESTED FOR THREATENING REP. JIM McDERMOTT?

ISOLATED.

THE GUY ARRESTED FOR THREATENING NANCY PELOSI?

ISOLATED.

Panel 4: THE WOULD-BE TIDES FOUNDATION KILLER WHO OPENLY CITES GLENN BECK AS AN INSPIRATION?

I-SO-LATED!!

HOLD ON... GOT A TEXT...

BA-DA-BOOP!

Panel 5: WOW, LISTEN TO THIS! LOUGHNER GAVE AN INTERVIEW--AND SAID THAT *OBAMA* IS HIS BIGGEST INFLUENCE, NEXT TO *SAUL ALINSKY* AND *STALIN*--AND THAT HIS MURDEROUS RAMPAGE WAS INSPIRED BY HIS SUPPORT FOR *HEALTH CARE REFORM!*

HA! I KNEW IT!

Panel 6: *I KNEW* HE HAD TO BE A LEFT-WING AMERICA-HATER! WELL, *THAT* CHANGES EVERYTHING, DOESN'T IT? HIS ACTIONS HAVE *UTTERLY DISCREDITED* OBAMA, NOT TO MENTION THE *ENTIRE DEMOCRAT PARTY*, AND--

--AND, UM--

UH--

Panel 7: THAT'S NOT WHAT THAT TEXT SAID AT ALL, IS IT?

HEH! NO, SORRY-- IT WAS BLINKY. HE'S GOING TO BE LATE FOR DINNER.

Panel 8: IF YOU THINK I'M EVEN GOING TO ACKNOWLEDGE THAT ANYTHING JUST OCCURRED, YOU'RE ENTIRELY MISTAKEN.

TRUST ME, THE THOUGHT NEVER CROSSED MY MIND.

TOM TOMORROW © 2011 ...www.thismodernworld.com...twitter.com/tomtomorrow

THIS MODERN WORLD

by TOM TOMORROW

KNOWING AND NOT KNOWING

THERE ARE THINGS YOU KNOW--

THIRTY-TWO DEGREES *FAHRENHEIT!*

--AND THINGS YOU DON'T KNOW--

--AND SOMETIMES EVEN THINGS YOU DON'T KNOW YOU KNOW.

THE--THE SQUARE OF THE *HYPOTENUSE!*

AS WE'VE SEEN LATELY, A LOT OF PEOPLE DON'T *WANT* TO KNOW THINGS THEY DON'T KNOW.

ACCORDING TO WIKILEAKS, OBAMA SECRETLY PRESSURED SPAIN TO DROP AN INVESTIGATION INTO BUSH'S TORTURE POLICIES--

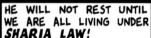

AUGGGH! STOP IT! WE'RE NOT *SUPPOSED* TO KNOW THINGS LIKE THAT!

VOTE

OR ELSE THEY *THINK* THEY KNOW THINGS THEY DO NOT ACTUALLY KNOW AT ALL.

GEORGE SOROS SECRETLY CONTROLS THE DEMOCRATS THROUGH FRONT GROUPS SUCH AS *ACORN* AND THE *NEW BLACK PANTHER PARTY!*

HE WILL NOT REST UNTIL WE ARE ALL LIVING UNDER *SHARIA LAW!*

IT'S A *FACT!*

REPUBLICANS IN CONGRESS CLEARLY KNOW *EXACTLY* WHAT *THEY* DON'T WANT TO KNOW.

AMERICANS DON'T NEED *HEALTH CARE!*

BIG BUSINESS CAN REGULATE *ITSELF!*

CLIMATE CHANGE IS A *HOAX!*

YOU COULD FILL A *BOOK* WITH THE THINGS *GLENN BECK* DOESN'T KNOW.

"A" BOOK? HA HA! TRY A HALF DOZEN BOOKS A *YEAR!*

YOU THINK I PAY MY GHOSTWRITERS TO SIT ON THEIR *HANDS?*

GLENN BECK

AND AMERICANS IN GENERAL ARE REMARKABLY ADEPT AT DECIDING *NOT* TO KNOW THINGS THEY *DO* KNOW, BUT WISH THEY DID NOT.

ACCORDING TO WIKILEAKS, THERE ARE SECRET GLASSES YOU CAN WEAR THAT EXPOSE OUR LEADERS AS *HORRIBLE ALIENS!*

HEY! WILL YOU *ZIP* IT, ALREADY? I TOLD YOU I AM *NOT INTERESTED!*

OBEY

TOM TOMORROW © 2011 ...www.thismodernworld.com...twitter.com/tomtomorrow

24

THIS MODERN WORLD

by TOM TOMORROW

TEA PARTY HISTORY LESSON

IN DAYS OF YORE, GIANTS STRODE THE EARTH...THE INFALLIBLE MEN WE KNOW AND WORSHIP TODAY AS THE *FOUNDING FATHERS!*

ALL MEN ARE CREATED EQUAL-- DON'T YOU *AGREE*, THOMAS JEFFERSON!

ABSOLUTELY, GEORGE WASHINGTON--GIVE OR TAKE 2/5THS!

THEY WERE PERSONALLY DIRECTED BY GOD ALMIGHTY TO CREATE HIS MOST FAVORITE NATION-STATE IN ALL OF HUMAN HISTORY!

DON'T TELL THE ISRAELITES--BUT THOU ART MY *TRUE* CHOSEN PEOPLE!

AWESOME!

GOD ALSO PROVIDED THEM WITH OUR HOLIEST OF SACRED DOCUMENTS-- THE ETERNAL, UNCHANGING *CONSTITUTION!*

LISTEN UP, PEOPLE! THIS IS GONNA BE A NATION WITH *LOW TAXES* AND *LOTS OF GUNS!*

THE MAN UPSTAIRS *SAID* SO!

AS MICHELE BACHMANN REMINDS US, OUR REMARKABLE FOUNDERS DID NOT REST UNTIL *SLAVERY* WAS *ENDED!*

ENJOY YOUR FORTY ACRES AND YOUR MULE, HARRIET TUBMAN!

THANKS, NOTED FOUNDING FATHER JOHN QUINCY ADAMS!

TWO CENTURIES LATER, MARTIN LUTHER KING JR. STRUGGLED BRAVELY TO UPHOLD THEIR LEGACY OF *EQUALITY FOR ALL!*

WE MUST KEEP OUR EYES ON THE *PRIZE*--A WORLD IN WHICH WHITE MALE CONSERVATIVES ARE *FREE AT LAST* FROM THE OPPRESSION THEY HAVE SO LONG ENDURED!

TODAY WE STRIVE TO *PROTECT* OUR FOUNDERS' HERITAGE--FROM THE FORCES OF *INCOMPREHENSIBLE EVIL* ALIGNED *AGAINST* IT!

HOW CLOSE ARE WE TO EXTINGUISHING THE FLAME OF LIBERTY ONCE AND FOR ALL, FRANCES FOX PIVEN?

VERY CLOSE INDEED, GEORGE SOROS! MY NEW ARTICLE IN "THE NATION" SHOULD *REALLY* GET THE BALL ROLLING!

EX-CELLENT! SAUL ALINSKY WOULD HAVE BEEN *PROUD!*

BOY, DO I HATE FREEDOM!

TOM TOMORROW ©2011 ...www.thismodernworld.com...twitter.com/tomtomorrow

THIS MODERN WORLD

by TOM TOMORROW

HELLO, SPARKY! ALLOW ME TO PRESENT MY LATEST CREATION-- THE *CONSERVABOT 9000!*

HE'S DESIGNED TO AGGREGATE CONSERVATIVE OPINION IN REAL TIME--AND PRESENT *US* WITH A COHERENT *SYNOPSIS!*

CONSERVABOT--PLEASE DISCUSS THE *EGYPTIAN UPRISING.*

WHIRRR-- CLICK!

?

DECLARATIVE: THE PROTESTS IN EGYPT VALIDATE THE LEGACY OF *GEORGE W. BUSH!* FREEDOM IS *FLOURISHING!* IT IS "DEMOCRACY, WHISKEY, SEXY" TIME ALL *OVER* AGAIN! WHIRRR!

PROCESSING!

UPDATING INPUT...*ALERT!* IF TRULY DEMOCRATIC ELECTIONS ARE HELD IN EGYPT, *MUSLIMS* ARE LIKELY TO PARTICIPATE--AND POSSIBLY EVEN *WIN!* CLICK--WHIRRR--

STAND BY!

PROCESSING! PROCESSING!

UH--YOU MIGHT WANT TO STEP BACK A LITTLE.

REVISED DECLARATIVE: THE UNACCEPTABLE TURMOIL IN EGYPT IS ENTIRELY THE FAULT OF *BARACK OBAMA*--A SECRET AMERICA-HATING *MUSLIM* WHOSE CLANDESTINE SUPPORT FOR AN ISLAMIC UPRISING WILL COST US AN IRREPLACABLE STRATEGIC *ALLY!*

PROCESSING! PROCESSING!

FURTHER ANALYSIS: THE *MUSLIM BROTHERHOOD* IS CONSPIRING WITH *BILL AYERS* AND *CODE PINK* TO IMPOSE A *CALIPHATE* FROM CAIRO TO *PARIS!* ALSO, OBAMA IS THE *REAL* DICTATOR!

PROCESSING! PROCESSING! *PROCESS*--

KA-BOOM!

"COHERENT" WAS PROBABLY ASKING TOO MUCH.

WITH THE BENEFIT OF HINDSIGHT, I'M INCLINED TO AGREE.

THIS MODERN WORLD

by TOM TOMORROW

THE ADVENTURES OF... MIDDLE MAN

A FEW SHORT DAYS AGO: FROM HIS SECRET H.Q. DEEP BENEATH THE WHITE HOUSE, MIDDLE-MAN CONFERS WITH HIS ERSTWHILE ALLY-- THE *EGYPTIAN STRONGMAN!*

FOR THIRTY YEARS, YOUR NATION FINANCED AND SUPPORTED ME-- POLITELY OVERLOOKING CORRUPTION AND REPRESSION ALL THE WHILE!

TWO-WAY VIDEO LINK

YOU YOURSELF CALLED ME A FRIEND--AND DELIBERATELY CHOSE **NOT** TO PRESSURE ME OVER ALL THAT **HUMAN RIGHTS** NONSENSE!

ER, YES, WELL--I BELIEVE IT IS TIME TO LOOK **FORWARD** RATHER THAN **BACKWARD!**

TWO-WAY VIDEO LINK

IN **FACT**--I WAS THINKING, IT MIGHT BE BEST IF YOU, UH, MAYBE STARTED THINKING ABOUT--OH, YOU KNOW--HOW CAN I PUT THIS--UH--

OH, **FINE! I GET** IT! IF IT'S REALLY WHAT EVERYONE WANTS--

TWO-WAY VIDEO LINK

--I'LL **DELEGATE** POWER TO MY NEW **SIDEKICK**--THE **DUNGEON MASTER!**

YOU MAY REMEMBER HIM--AS THE CIA'S POINT MAN IN EGYPT ON **EXTRAORDINARY RENDITIONS!**

ALWAYS HAPPY TO HELP A **FRIEND!**

BUT **SUDDENLY...**

WHOOPS! CHANGE OF PLANS! MY GENERALS INFORM ME I'LL BE STEPPING DOWN ENTIRELY-- EFFECTIVE **IMMEDIATELY!**

UH OH! MUST...COMPOSE... **STATEMENT!** HAVEN'T GOT A MOMENT...TO **LOSE!**

MIDDLE-MAN **SPRINGS** INTO ACTION!

TWO-WAY VIDEO LINK

AND A FEW HOURS LATER...

EVENTS HAVE, UH, OCCURRED! HISTORY HAS, UM, BEEN MADE! AND JUST TO BE CLEAR, WE BARELY EVEN **KNEW** THAT STRONGMAN GUY!

REMEMBER--OUR SUPPORT FOR DEMOCRACY IS **STEADFAST!**

WHEN IT'S, YOU KNOW, CONVENIENT.

YAY, FREEDOM!

UNDOUBTEDLY TO BE **CONTINUED!**

TOM TOMORROW © 2011 ...www.thismodernworld.com...twitter.com/tomtomorrow

27

THIS MODERN WORLD

by TOM TOMORROW

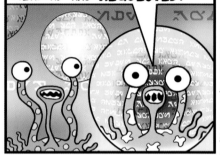

THIS MODERN WORLD

by TOM TOMORROW

NUCLEAR SAFETY
EXPLAINED BY THE INVISIBLE HAND OF THE FREE MARKET

IF HE'S INVISIBLE, HOW COME--

SERIOUSLY, DO I HAVE TO EXPLAIN THE MAGIC OF THE MARKET EVERY TIME I GO *OUTSIDE*?

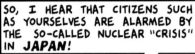

SO, I HEAR THAT CITIZENS SUCH AS YOURSELVES ARE ALARMED BY THE SO-CALLED NUCLEAR "CRISIS" IN *JAPAN!*

WELL, YES, IT DOES MAKE US WONDER HOW SAFE--

EXCUSE ME--ARE YOU *NUCLEAR SCIENTISTS*?

ER-- WHAT?

BECAUSE UNLESS YOU HAVE ADVANCED DEGREES IN NUCLEAR PHYSICS, NO ONE IS *INTERESTED* IN YOUR UNINFORMED OPINIONS!

EVERY ENERGY SOURCE HAS SOME DEGREE OF RISK! THE BLADE OF A WIND TURBINE MIGHT COME LOOSE AND *DECAPITATE* YOU! DID YOU EVER THINK OF *THAT*?

I--UH--

I DIDN'T *THINK* SO!

OKAY, BUT STILL--AMERICAN NUCLEAR PLANTS *ARE* AGING, AND POORLY REGULATED--

REGULATION--*HAH!* THE INVISIBLE HAND OF THE FREE MARKET *LAUGHS* AT YOUR CHILDLIKE YEARNING FOR "REGULATION"!

LOOK, YOU HAVE *TWO CHOICES!* YOU CAN EITHER ACCEPT THE NUCLEAR INDUSTRY AS IT EXISTS *TODAY*--WITHOUT *ANY* FURTHER IMPROVEMENT OR OVERSIGHT--

--*OR* YOU CAN LIVE IN A COAL-BURNING DICKENSIAN *NIGHTMARE* FULL OF STREET URCHINS WITH *BLACK LUNG DISEASE!* IS *THAT* WHAT YOU WANT?

IS IT??

ER--OKAY THEN! NO MORE QUESTIONS FROM *US!*

I GUESS WE'LL BE *GOING* NOW!

EXCELLENT! THE IRREFUTABLE WISDOM OF THE FREE MARKET TRIUMPHS ONCE *AGAIN!*

NEXT

SO I HEAR YOU'RE WORRIED ABOUT *E-COLI* IN YOUR *FOOD*?

TOM TOMORROW © 2011 ....www.thismodernworld.com....twitter.com/tomtomorrow

THIS MODERN WORLD

by TOM TOMORROW

IT'S TIME ONCE AGAIN FOR THE ADVENTURES OF **CONSERVATIVE JONES, BOY DETECTIVE**--

Detective H.Q.

Keep Out

--AND HIS PERENNIALLY PERPLEXED SIDEKICK, "**MOONBAT**"!

COME IN, MOONBAT! YOUR TIMING IS, AS ALWAYS, **IMPECCABLE!**

I **REALLY** WISH YOU'D STOP CALLING ME THAT--

SILENCE, MOONBAT! I'M ABOUT TO SOLVE THE MYSTERY OF OPERATION **ODYSSEY DAWN!**

HUH. WELL I'M GUESSING YOU DON'T MEAN THE MYSTERY OF HOW WE CAN ALWAYS AFFORD TO SPEND HUNDREDS OF MILLIONS OF DOLLARS ON ANOTHER WAR WITHOUT GIVING IT A SECOND **THOUGHT**--

--AND YET, ALLEGEDLY CANNOT AFFORD SCHOOLTEACHERS' **SALARIES** OR HEATING SUBSIDIES FOR THE **ELDERLY?**

OH, **MOONBAT**--

--HOW DELIGHTFUL IT MUST BE, TO LIVE INSIDE THAT STRANGE, KALEIDOSCOPIC WONDERLAND YOU CALL A **BRAIN!**

NO, **I** WAS PURSUING THE MYSTERY OF HOW AN EFFEMINATE DEMOCRAT PRESIDENT COULD DO SOMETHING AS **MANLY** AS **BOMB ANOTHER COUNTRY**--AND I THINK I'VE FIGURED IT **OUT**--

OH, DO TELL.

--HE WAS **HENPECKED** INTO IT-- BY THE EMASCULATING **WOMEN** AROUND HIM!

YOU KNOW, THESE LITTLE TALKS OF OURS ARE ALWAYS SO ENLIGHTENING.

WATCH AND LEARN, MOONBAT--WATCH AND **LEARN!**

NEXT: CONSERVATIVE'S **CONUNDRUM!**

HOW TO SUPPORT **BOMBS**--

--WITHOUT SUPPORTING **OBAMA??!**

...www.thismodernworld.com...twitter.com/tomtomorrow

TOM TOMORROW ©2011

THIS MODERN WORLD

by TOM TOMORROW

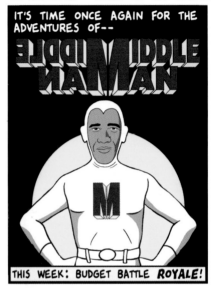

IT'S TIME ONCE AGAIN FOR THE ADVENTURES OF--

MIDDLE-MAN

THIS WEEK: BUDGET BATTLE *ROYALE!*

WITH A GOVERNMENT SHUTDOWN LOOMING, MIDDLE-MAN CONFRONTS HIS ESTEEMED ARCH-RIVAL, *CAPTAIN ORANGE!*

IN THE INTERESTS OF BIPARTISAN COMPROMISE, I CAN AGREE TO *TEN BILLION DOLLARS* IN PAINFUL BUDGET CUTS!

I WON'T SETTLE FOR ANYTHING LESS THAN *THIRTY-TWO* BILLION!

SUDDENLY--THE *TEA PARTY PATRIOT* JUMPS INTO THE FRAY!

HOLD IT RIGHT *THERE*, MIDDLE-MAN! DID HE SAY *THIRTY-TWO* BILLION? HE MEANT *SIXTY-ONE* BILLION!

?

I DID? I MEAN, UH, RIGHT--I *DID!*

MIDDLE-MAN RETREATS TO HIS SECRET UNDERGROUND HIDEOUT-- THE *PRE-EMPTIVE CAVE...*

IF MY ESTEEMED ARCH-RIVALS ARE GOING TO MOVE THE *GOAL POST* IN THE MIDDLE OF OUR NEGOTIATIONS, THERE'S ONLY ONE THING TO *DO*--

--*MEET THEM HALFWAY!*

OR MORE.

TWO-WAY VIDEO LINK

AND SO...

ALL RIGHT, CAPTAIN ORANGE--I *INSIST* YOU ACCEPT *THIRTY-THREE* BILLION DOLLARS IN PAINFUL BUDGET CUTS!

CURSE YOU, MIDDLE-MAN! YOU'VE DEFEATED ME *AGAIN!* WHAT CHOICE DO I *HAVE* BUT TO ACCEPT--

---

BUT *THEN*--

HOLD IT RIGHT *THERE*, MIDDLE-MAN! WE'RE NOT SETTLING FOR ANYTHING LESS THAN THE *COMPLETE REPEAL* OF HEALTH CARE REFORM--*AND* DEFUNDING OF PLANNED PARENTHOOD--*AND*--

!

UH, MICHELE--A WORD, PLEASE?

THIS MODERN WORLD

by TOM TOMORROW

LANGUAGE IS A VIRUS

AN OCCASIONAL LOOK AT THE WAYS IN WHICH REALLY TERRIBLE IDEAS INFECT MAINSTREAM POLITICAL DISCOURSE

STEP ONE: REPUBLICAN POLITICIAN MAKES A *MODEST PROPOSAL*.

TO PAY FOR TAX CUTS FOR THE WEALTHY, I BELIEVE WE SHOULD *EUTHANIZE* THE ELDERLY--

--AND THEN PROCESS THEM INTO *TASTY SNACK CRACKERS!*

THE PROFITS FROM WHICH CAN BE USED TO FINANCE FURTHER TAX CUTS FOR THE WEALTHY.

SEE, IT'S *ENVIRONMENTAL!* IT'S "GREEN"!

I DON'T KNOW WHAT THE "SOYLENT" PART MEANS.

SOYLENT GREEN SNACK CRACKERS

STEP TWO: SERIOUS PEOPLE APPLAUD THE SERIOUSNESS OF THE PLAN.

IT'S *EXTREMELY* COURAGEOUS!

PROCESSING THE ELDERLY INTO SNACK CRACKERS HAS *ALWAYS* BEEN THE THIRD RAIL OF AMERICAN POLITICS!

STEP THREE: LEFT-WING CRITICS ARE PORTRAYED AS NAIVE, UNREALISTIC *IDEOLOGUES*.

IF THEY HAD *THEIR* WAY, GOVERNMENT WOULD BE REQUIRED TO PROVIDE CRADLE-TO-GRAVE *PONIES* AND *RAINBOWS!*

THEY ARE SO UNSERIOUS, IT IS BARELY WORTH ACKNOWLEDGING THEIR *EXISTENCE!*

STEP FOUR: THE WINDOW OF ACCEPTABLE DEBATE IS SHIFTED EVER FURTHER TOWARD OUTRIGHT LUNACY.

PERHAPS WE COULD TAKE A MORE *MODERATE* APPROACH--AND SIMPLY ABANDON THE ELDERLY IN THE DESERT TO FEND FOR *THEMSELVES!*

THAT'S ABOUT WHAT I'D *EXPECT*--FROM A BIG GOVERNMENT SOCIALIST LIKE *YOU!*

TOM TOMORROW © 2011 ... www.thismodernworld.com...twitter.com/tomtomorrow

35

Panel 1:

HELLO, SPARKY! AS YOU CAN SEE, I'VE REPAIRED THE *CONSERVA-BOT* 9000!

GREETINGS, LIBTARD!

HEH HEH! I ALSO TWEAKED HIS PERSONALITY SETTINGS SLIGHTLY.

SWELL!

Panel 2:

DECLARATIVE: YOU CANNOT BALANCE THE BUDGET BY RAISING TAXES ON THE RICH--BECAUSE THERE ARE *NOT ENOUGH WEALTHY HUMANOIDS!*

SIGH...YOU'RE GOING TO MAKE ME ARGUE WITH YOUR ROBOT, AREN'T YOU?

THINK OF IT AS A TURING TEST!

Panel 3:

OKAY, LOOK--THE QUESTION ISN'T HOW MANY RICH PEOPLE THERE *ARE*--IT'S HOW MUCH WEALTH THEY *CONTROL.*

IN 2007, THE TOP 1% OF HOUSEHOLDS OWNED 35% OF THE WEALTH. THE NEXT 19% OWNED ANOTHER 50%--

--LEAVING A WHOPPING 15% FOR THE REMAINING 80% OF THE POPULATION.

IT'S ONLY GOTTEN WORSE SINCE THEN.

Panel 4:

ON TOP OF *THAT*, A RECENT STUDY FROM THE G.A.O. SAYS THAT MOST *CORPORATIONS* PAY *NO* U.S. TAXES AT *ALL!*

IF ELMINATING DEFICITS IS *REALLY* THE GOAL--AS OPPOSED TO ELIMINATING PROGRAMS CONSERVATIVES DON'T LIKE--THE ANSWER COULDN'T BE MORE STRAIGHTFORWARD.

Panel 5:

PROCESSING!

PROCESSING!

Panel 6:

DECLARATIVE: YOUR EMOTIONAL ATTACHMENT AND/OR LOYALTY TO THE NATION-STATE IN WHICH WE RESIDE IS *HIGHLY SUSPECT!*

AND YOU ARE PROBABLY *HOMOSEXUAL!*

WELL, HE RESPONDS LIKE A REAL RIGHT WINGER, I'LL GIVE YOU THAT.

HAH! MY GENIUS TRIUMPHS *AGAIN!*

THIS MODERN WORLD

by TOM TOMORROW

TWO GUYS STANDING ON AN INCLINE

ANOTHER IN AN OCCASIONAL SERIES OF UNSUBTLE VISUAL METAPHORS

WE ONLY INTERVENED IN LIBYA TO PREVENT A HUMANITARIAN DISASTER.

REGIME CHANGE IS *NOT* ON THE AGENDA.

ANYWAY, WE'RE JUST ONE PART OF THE NATO COALITION.

AND IT WILL ALL BE OVER IN DAYS, NOT WEEKS.

WELL, IT MIGHT TAKE A *FEW* WEEKS--BUT THERE WILL *DEFINITELY* NOT BE ANY AMERICAN BOOTS ON THE GROUND!

EXCEPT FOR THE CIA, WHICH HAS BEEN ON THE GROUND FROM THE START.

OH, AND OBAMA SAYS NATO MUST MAINTAIN OPERATIONS UNTIL GADDAFI IS OUT OF POWER.

SO I GUESS REGIME CHANGE IS SORT OF ON THE AGENDA AFTER ALL.

YOU KNOW, THIS INCLINE WE'RE STANDING ON DOESN'T SEEM TO PROVIDE MUCH TRACTION.

SOMETIMES INCLINES ARE LIKE THAT.

TOM TOMORROW ©2011 ...www.thismodernworld.com...twitter.com/tomtomorrow

THIS MODERN WORLD

by TOM TOMORROW

Panel 1:
SOMETIME IN 2008 OR SO, A RUMOR BEGINS TO CIRCULATE.

GIVEN HIS OTHERWORLDLY DEMEANOR AND PRETER-NATURAL CALM--

--HOW CAN WE BE SURE OBAMA WAS *REALLY* BORN ON THE PLANET *EARTH*?

Panel 2:
WITHIN A FEW YEARS THE SO-CALLED "EARTHERS" ARE EVERYWHERE.

WHAT *BETTER* WAY FOR A SHAPE-SHIFTING ALIEN TO INFILTRATE AND CONQUER OUR SOCIETY--

--THAN TO POSE AS A BLACK INFANT BORN TO IMPOVERISHED PARENTS IN 1961!

IT EXPLAINS SO *MUCH*!

Panel 3:
AND THEN A PUBLICITY HUNGRY LUNATIC JUMPS INTO THE FRAY.

THE "EARTHERS" RAISE SOME *VERY* INTERESTING QUESTIONS!

WHY *WON'T* OBAMA RE-LEASE A DNA SAMPLE? DOES HE HAVE SOME-THING TO *HIDE*?

Panel 4:
NOT ONLY *THAT*--BUT I HEARD HE WASN'T A VERY GOOD *STUDENT*! SO HOW'D HE GET INTO *HARVARD*, ANYWAY?

WITH THE HELP OF AN *ALIEN MIND CONTROL RAY*, MAYBE?

I'M JUST *ASKIN'*!

Panel 5:
BUT *THEN*--

--THE PRESIDENT HAS SUPPLIED DNA--PROVING THAT HE *IS* HUMAN!

I REPEAT--THE PRESIDENT OF THE UNITED STATES *IS* A HUMAN BEING!

WHAT A *STUNNING* DEVELOPMENT!

Panel 6:
REPUBLICANS SCRAMBLE TO CHANGE THE SUBJECT...

HOW DO WE KNOW OBAMA DIDN'T START THE RUMOR *HIMSELF*--IN ORDER TO MAKE CONSERVATIVES *LOOK* BAD?

CLEARLY WE ARE THE REAL VICTIMS HERE.

Panel 7:
...WHILE DIEHARD "EARTH-ERS" REMAIN UNCONVINCED.

THIS PROVES *NOTHING*! DO YOU KNOW HOW EASY IT WOULD BE FOR AN ADVANCED ALIEN SPECIES TO REPLICATE A LITTLE HUMAN DNA?

VERY EASY *INDEED*!

Panel 8:
NONE OF IT HAS *ANY-THING* TO DO WITH RACE, OF COURSE.

HEY--ALL WE'RE SAYING IS THAT THE PRESIDENT IS A STRANGE, DARK-SKINNED, ALIEN *OTHER*!

UH--IXNAY ON THE ARKDAY INSKAY.

OOPS--DID I SAY THAT OUT LOUD?

HEH HEH.

TOM TOMORROW ©2011 ...www.thismodernworld.com....twitter.com/tomtomorrow

THIS MODERN WORLD

by TOM TOMORROW

THE TOP SECRET 100% TRUE STORY OF GEORGE W. BUSH: TIME TRAVELER!

AT A CIA "BLACK SITE" IN 2002.

WHERE IS THE "TICKING TIME BOMB"? I WANT ANSWERS *NOW!*

I DON'T KNOW WHAT YOU'RE *TALKING* ABOUT! BUT I *DO* KNOW WHERE OSAMA IS PLANNING TO SET UP A *SAFEHOUSE*-- IN FIVE OR TEN *YEARS!*

THE OVAL OFFICE, APRIL, 2011.

GEORGE W. BUSH?? WHAT--?!

LISTEN *CLOSELY!* I'M FROM THE YEAR 2002-- AND THANKS TO THE UNAMBIGUOUS SUCCESS OF MY *INTERROGATION* POLICY, I KNOW WHERE *YOU* CAN FIND BIN LADEN!

SHORTLY THEREAFTER...

EXCELLENT WORK, EVERYONE! BUT REMEMBER--NO ONE CAN *EVER* KNOW THAT I WAS HERE! DON'T LET THAT STAFF PHOTOGRAPHER IN THE ROOM UNTIL THE TEMPORAL DISPLACEMENT *SUBSIDES!*

NOW IF YOU'LL *EXCUSE* ME--I'M LATE FOR A SPEECH--IN 2003!

NEXT STOP: THE U.S.S. LINCOLN, APRIL, 2003!

HEH HEH! IF YOUR VIEW OF TIME WASN'T SO PATHETICALLY *LINEAR,* YOU'D UNDERSTAND HOW TRUE THAT BANNER REALLY *IS!*

BEG YOUR PARDON, SIR?

ER--I SAID, GREAT JOB! KEEP UP THE GOOD WORK!

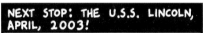

MISSION ACCOMPLISHED

UH-- YES, SIR!

THEN--THE *PRESENT DAY*...

DAMMIT GEORGE--IT'S NOT *FAIR* THAT OBAMA GETS ALL THE CREDIT WHEN *YOU* DID ALL THE *WORK!*

THAT'S THE WAY IT HAS TO *BE,* DICK! NOW I'M OFF TO 2001--TO GET THE WAR IN AFGHANISTAN *STARTED!*

IT MIGHT SEEM LIKE A POINTLESS WASTE *NOW*--

--BUT IT ALL MAKES SENSE-- IN THE *32ND CENTURY!*

TOM TOMORROW © 2011 ...www.thismodernworld.com...twitter.com/tomtomorrow

This Modern World

by Tom Tomorrow

And so it came to pass that the terrifying Bogeyman who had haunted their dreams for so very long was slain in his lair.

NO **LONGER** SHALL WE COWER, FEARFUL THAT **HE** MAY BE HIDING IN THE CLOSET OR UNDER THE **BED**--

--WAITING TO KILL US **ALL**!

AND/OR IMPOSE SHARIA LAW.

The leader of the nation-state recognized that a moment of opportunity was at hand.

IT IS TIME TO **END** THIS "WAR ON THINGS THAT CAUSE US TERROR"--AND BRING OUR WEARY ARMIES **HOME** FROM THEIR DISTANT BATTLES!

SERIOUSLY, IT'S BEEN TEN YEARS.

ENOUGH IS ENOUGH.

The people began to re-assess their priorities.

NOW THAT WE NO LONGER SPEND UNIMAGINABLE **FORTUNES** ON PERPETUAL, POINTLESS **WARS**--

--WE CAN INSTEAD FUND **SCHOOLS**--CREATE **JOBS**--REBUILD OUR CRUMBLING ROADS AND **BRIDGES**!

WHY DIDN'T WE THINK OF THIS **SOONER**?

Emboldened by success, the leader confronted other problems bedeviling his land.

WE SHALL **HALT** THE MENACE OF GLOBAL CLIMATE CHANGE--**OVERCOME** OUR ADDICTION TO FOSSIL FUELS--AND INSTITUTE A SYSTEM OF **TRULY** UNIVERSAL HEALTH CARE!

BECAUSE **OUR** NATION-STATE CAN DO WHATEVER WE SET OUR MIND TO!

And they all lived happily ever after.

THANK **GOODNESS** THE DEATH OF THE TERRIFYING BOGEYMAN LED US TO RECONSIDER OUR COMMITMENT TO THE POLITICS OF **FEAR**!

HOW **TRAGIC** IT WOULD HAVE BEEN TO CONTINUE DOWN **THAT** ILL-CONSIDERED PATH!

UM, SPARKY--

--YOU'RE NOT **EDITORIALIZING** AGAIN, ARE YOU?

WHAT? OF COURSE NOT! IT'S JUST AN **INNOCENT** BEDTIME FABLE!

NOW GO TO SLEEP.

SO DID THE LEADER CLOSE GUANTANAMO?

UH--SURE HE DID.

TOM TOMORROW ©2011 ...www.thismodernworld.com...twitter.com/tomtomorrow

THIS MODERN WORLD

by TOM TOMORROW

Panel 1:

CANDIDATE OBAMA SAID WHISTLE-BLOWERS WERE *PATRIOTS* WHO SHOULD BE *ENCOURAGED!*

AND RIGHTLY SO! WITHOUT WHISTLEBLOWERS, WE'D HAVE NEVER LEARNED ABOUT *ABU GHRAIB* OR *WARRANTLESS WIRETAPPING!*

Panel 2:

BUT THE OBAMA ADMINISTRATION HAS ALL BUT DECLARED *WAR* ON WHISTLEBLOWERS!

THEY'VE INVOKED THE *ESPIONAGE ACT* IN FIVE CASES-- WHICH, AS JANE MAYER NOTES IN THE NEW YORKER, IS MORE TIMES "THAN HAVE OCCURRED IN ALL PREVIOUS ADMINISTRATIONS *COMBINED!*"

Panel 3:

IN THAT SAME ARTICLE, A CONSERVATIVE POLITICAL SCIENTIST--WHO *SUPPORTS* MORE STRINGENT PROTECTION OF CLASSIFIED MATERIAL-- DECLARES THAT "OBAMA HAS PRESIDED OVER THE MOST DRACONIAN CRACKDOWN ON LEAKS IN OUR HISTORY--EVEN MORESO THAN *NIXON!*"

RIBBIT!

Panel 4:

AND YALE LAW PROFESSOR JACK BALKIN SAYS THAT "WE ARE WITNESSING THE BIPARTISAN NORMALIZATION AND LEGITIMIZATION OF A *NATIONAL SURVEILLANCE STATE!*"

I GUESS THESE THINGS JUST SNEAK UP ON YOU SO GRADUALLY SOMETIMES, YOU DON'T EVEN REALIZE WHAT'S *HAPPENING* 'TIL IT'S TOO LATE.

Panel 5:

Panel 6:

YOU KNOW, IT'S ACTUALLY A *MYTH* THAT FROGS WILL REMAIN IN A POT OF SLOWLY-HEATED WATER UNTIL THEY BOIL TO DEATH.

COME *BACK* HERE! YOU'RE SPOILING A *PERFECTLY GOOD METAPHOR!*

Tom Tomorrow © 2011 ...www.thismodernworld.com ...twitter.com/tomtomorrow

THIS MODERN WORLD

by TOM TOMORROW

HOW CAN THERE BE **GLOBAL WARMING**--WHEN I HAD TO SPEND SO MUCH TIME LAST WINTER SHOVELING **SNOW**?

HA HA! GOOD POINT!

NEVER MIND THAT THOSE RECORD SNOWFALLS WERE FOLLOWED BY RECORD **RAINFALL**--NOT TO MENTION RECORD **FLOODS**!

AND NEVER MIND THAT WE'RE HAVING SUCH A FREAKISH AND DEVASTATING **TORNADO SEASON**! OR THAT TEXAS IS EXPERIENCING THE WORST DROUGHT IN RECENT **HISTORY**!

AND SO **WHAT** IF WE'VE JUST HAD NINE OF THE TEN HOTTEST YEARS EVER **RECORDED**? HOW COULD ANY OF THAT **POSSIBLY** INDICATE A CHANGING GLOBAL **CLIMATE**?

CRAZY **LIBERALS**!

AND SCIENTISTS.

WELL YOU OBVIOUSLY CAN'T DRAW LONG-TERM CONCLUSIONS FROM A HANDFUL OF ISOLATED EVENTS.

RIGHT. HOW SHORTSIGHTED OF ME.

TOM TOMORROW ©2011 ...www.thismodernworld.com...twitter.com/tomtomorrow

42

THIS MODERN WORLD

by TOM TOMORROW

Panel 1: JUST IN TIME FOR SUMMER--IT'S THE LATEST *STUPID MEDIA DISTRACTION*--

THE POLITICIAN'S PENIS

THE MOST SHOCKING SEX SCANDAL WITH NO APPARENT SEX EVER

Panel 2: IT'S A SCANDAL BOILED DOWN TO THE MOST BASIC POSSIBLE COMPONENTS: (1) A PENIS, AND (2) A POLITICIAN LYING ABOUT IT.

MY ACCOUNT WAS *HACKED!* I'VE NEVER SEEN THAT PENIS BEFORE IN MY *LIFE!*

AS FAR AS I KNOW.

I MEAN, WHO CAN EVER BE CERTAIN OF *ANYTHING*?

?

Panel 3: THE POLITICIAN'S SUPPORTERS TRY TO EXPLAIN THE PENIS AWAY.

THERE ARE *MILLIONS* OF PENISES ON THE INTERNET! HOW CAN YOU PROVE THIS ONE IS *HIS*?

IT MIGHT NOT EVEN BE A PENIS AT *ALL*--BUT RATHER, A PHOTOSHOPPED *CUCUMBER*. OR POSSIBLY A BANANA.

OR A BABY'S ARM HOLDING AN APPLE!

WHAT?

Panel 4: BUT AS IT TURNS OUT, THE RIGHT WING PROVOCATEUR WHO BROKE THE STORY WAS TELLING THE TRUTH FOR ONCE.

HAH! FORGET ABOUT THE ACORN VIDEOS AND THAT SHIRLEY SHERROD BUSINESS!

FROM NOW ON, WHEN PEOPLE THINK OF ANDREW BREITBART--THEY WILL THINK ONLY OF A *PENIS!*

PSST--WANNA SEE AN EVEN *BETTER* SHOT?

CENSORED

Panel 5: ULTIMATELY THE POLITICIAN ACKNOWLEDGES OWNERSHIP OF THE PENIS... AND LEADERS OF HIS OWN PARTY CALL ON HIM TO *RESIGN!*

WHAT WILL HAPPEN *NOW*? SPECULATION IS *RAMPANT* AMONG JOURNALISTS THRILLED TO GET MORE MILEAGE OUT OF PENISGATE!

NOT TO MENTION *CARTOONISTS* LOOKING FOR *CHEAP LAUGHS!*

TALK ABOUT *BOTTOM FEEDERS!*

Panel 6: COMING UP--THE SEASON'S *NEXT* STUPID MEDIA DISTRACTION!

WILL IT BE KILLER *SHARKS*? A DRUG-ABUSING *CELEBRITY*? MORE *PENISES*?

WE WON'T KNOW 'TIL IT GETS HERE--WHICH SHOULD BE ANY *MINUTE* NOW!

BUT FIRST, THESE MESSAGES!

DID YOU JUST TEXT ME A *PHOTO*?

©2011 ...www.thismodernworld.com

TOM TOMORROW

44

THIS MODERN WORLD

by TOM TOMORROW

WELCOME TO THE NEVER-ENDING CONSERVATIVE CARNIVAL OF CRAZY

FUN AND GAMES FOR THE WHOLE *FAMILY!*

HIT THE TARGET--AND WE'LL GIVE YOUR PRIZE TO A *RICH PERSON!*

MAKES SENSE! AFTER ALL, *I* MIGHT BE RICH SOME-DAY--AND THEN *I'LL* GET PRIZES!

ABORTION DOCTOR

LIBERAL

TAKE A RIDE THROUGH THE EVER-POPULAR *TUNNEL OF FEAR!*

HOMOSEXUALS WANT TO DESTROY TRADITIONAL *MARRIAGE!*

TERROR-ISTS ARE LURKING *EVERY-WHERE!!*

BWAH HA HA HA

IN THE G.O.P. HOUSE OF MIRRORS--*NOTHING* IS WHAT IT SEEMS!

REPUBLICANS ARE FIGHTING TO *SAVE MEDICARE*--FROM THE *DEMOCRATS!*

IT'S *TRUE!*

VISIT THE PRESIDENTIAL CANDIDATE *FREAK SHOW*--IF YOU *DARE!*

WORLD'S LEAST SELF-AWARE HUMAN BEING

THE IN-CREDIBLE IMPLODING CANDIDATE

AND CELEBRATE *LIBERTY*--ON OUR COMPLETELY UNREGULATED *FREE MARKET THRILL RIDES!**

AIIIIEEEEEEEE!

AT LEAST THEY'LL DIE FREE FROM THE TYRANNY OF OPPRESSIVE GOVERNMENT SAFETY INSPECTIONS!

WE SHOULD *ALL* BE SO LUCKY!

*PLEASE REMEMBER TO SIGN LIABILITY WAIVERS ON YOUR WAY IN.

TOM TOMORROW©2011 ...www.thismodernworld.com...twitter.com/tomtomorrow

THIS MODERN WORLD

by TOM TOMORROW

LIBYA MADE SIMPLE
FEATURING "CHUCKLES" THE SENSIBLE WOODCHUCK

BASICALLY, THE WAR IN LIBYA IS **NOT** A WAR AT **ALL!**

THAT'S RIGHT! IT'S **REALLY** MORE OF A CONDITIONAL HUMANITARIAN KINETIC MILITARY KIND OF, UM, ACTIONY THING.

SO OBAMA IS **OBVIOUSLY** NOT SUBJECT TO THE REQUIREMENTS OF THE WAR POWERS RESOLUTION!

IT'S **EXTREMELY** CLEAR CUT! NOBODY WITH ANY **REAL** KNOWLEDGE DISAGREES!

WELL, EXCEPT FOR ERIC HOLDER, AND THE TOP ATTORNEYS AT THE OFFICE OF LEGAL COUNSEL AND THE DEPARTMENT OF DEFENSE.

WHATEVER! THERE'S ALWAYS GOING TO BE **SOMEBODY** WHO DISAGREES!

BUT THE FACT REMAINS: WITH NO AMERICAN TROOPS IN HARM'S WAY, THERE ARE TECHNICALLY **NO** **HOSTILITIES!**

AND THEREFORE NO **WAR!** END OF **DISCUSSION!**

OF COURSE, BY THAT LOGIC, A **NUCLEAR FIRST STRIKE** WOULDN'T REALLY COUNT AS WAR, EITHER.

SERIOUSLY, DON'T OVERTHINK IT.

TOM TOMORROW ©2011 ...www.thismodernworld.com...twitter.com/tomtomorrow

THIS MODERN WORLD

by TOM TOMORROW

HOLOGRAPHIC TEACHING INTERFACE **ACTIVATED!** GOOD MORNING, CHILDREN! TODAY WE'LL CONTINUE OUR STUDY OF YOUR 21ST CENTURY ANCESTORS-- KNOWN TO HISTORIANS AS THE **WANKIEST GENERATION!**

YOUR ANCESTORS WERE DEFINED BY THREE PRIMARY CHARACTERISTICS: THEIR UNSHAKABLE ADDICTION TO **OIL**...THEIR IRRATIONAL SUBSERVIENCE TO THE **RICH**...AND, OF COURSE, THEIR ALL-CONSUMING, ENDLESS **FEAR.**

LIKE TYPICAL ADDICTS, THEY REFUSED TO ADMIT THEY EVEN **HAD** A PROBLEM! FOR INSTANCE, THEY INSISTED THAT THEIR MULTIPLE, ENDLESS WARS, IN ONE OF THE PLANET'S PRIMARY OIL-PRODUCING REGIONS, ACTUALLY HAD **NOTHING TO DO WITH OIL!**

TRY TO STIFLE YOUR LAUGHTER, PLEASE.

THEY WERE SPENDING AT LEAST TWO BILLION DOLLARS A WEEK ON THESE WARS--WHICH WOULD BE ABOUT $700 **KATRILLION** IN **TODAY'S** CURRENCY! AND YET, THEY SIMULTANEOUSLY DECIDED THAT WHAT THEY **REALLY** NEEDED AS A SOCIETY...WERE **LARGE TAX CUTS** FOR THE **WEALTHY!**

YOU SEE, YOUR ANCESTORS APPRENTLY BELIEVED THAT THE PRIMARY **PURPOSE** OF SOCIETY WAS TO REDISTRIBUTE THEIR NATION'S WEALTH--TO THOSE WHO ALREADY POSSESSED **MOST** OF IT! ALL OTHER CONSIDERATIONS WERE **SECONDARY!**

YOU CAN IMAGINE HOW WELL THAT WORKED OUT.

FINALLY, WE MUSTN'T OVERLOOK THEIR OVERWHELMING, CONSTANT, INCHOATE **FEAR**--THAT SOME BAD THING **MIGHT** HAPPEN SOMEDAY! IN RETROSPECT, IT'S CLEAR THAT CIVIL LIBERTIES AND THE RULE OF LAW NEVER STOOD A **CHANCE** AGAINST THEIR COLLECTIVE, SOCIETAL **ANXIETY DISORDER!**

THE ULTIMATE LEGACY OF THEIR MALIGNANT STEWARDSHIP OF THIS ONCE-THRIVING NATION WAS, OF COURSE, A HELLISH AND DYSFUNCTIONAL POST-APOCALYPTIC **NIGHTMARE**--OR, AS YOU BIOLOGICALS CALL IT, **"DAILY LIFE!"**

AND THAT'S ALL OUR TIME FOR TODAY! WE'LL CONTINUE NEXT WEEK-- AT LEAST, WITH THOSE OF YOU WHO HAVEN'T BEEN CAPTURED BY **ORGAN HARVESTERS** OR SOLD TO **MUTANT SLAVERS!**

BEST OF **LUCK!**

BUH-BYE!

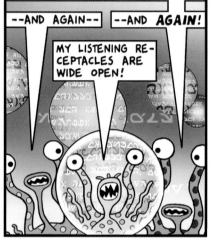

THIS MODERN WORLD

by TOM TOMORROW

MIDDLE-MAN

THIS WEEK: DEBT LIMIT DEBACLE!

PROLOGUE: LAST DECEMBER...

--SO WE'LL COMPROMISE--BY **EXTENDING** THE BUSH TAX CUTS! AND NO NEED TO DISCUSS THE IMMINENT **DEBT CEILING** PROBLEM--I'M **SURE** YOU FELLOWS WILL DO THE RIGHT THING WHEN THE TIME COMES!

WE WILL? I MEAN, OF COURSE WE WILL!

HEH, HEH!

PRESENT DAY: MIDDLE-MAN INTERCEPTS A **SHOCKING** TRANSMISSION!

--SO WE'VE DECIDED TO HOLD THE DEBT CEILING **HOSTAGE**--UNTIL WE GET EVEN **MORE** OF WHAT WE WANT!

GASP! **NO ONE** COULD HAVE FORESEEN **THIS!**

LIVE VIDEO FEED

HE LEAPS INTO ACTION--READY ONCE AGAIN TO DEPLOY THE AWESOME POWER OF **PRE-EMPTIVE COMPROMISE!**

I'M PUTTING **SOCIAL SECURITY** AND **MEDICARE** ON THE TABLE!

YOU'RE TOO CLEVER FOR **US**, MIDDLE-MAN!

BY HALF!

BUT CAPTAIN ORANGE AND THE HUMAN TURTLE FIND THEMSELVES TRAPPED BETWEEN RIVAL FACTIONS OF THEIR **OWN PARTY!**

WALL **STREET** SAYS **DEAL!**

THE **TEA PARTY** SAYS **NO DEAL!**

ULP!

!

AND **THEN**--THE **CANT-MAN** ENTERS THE FRAY!

UM--MAYBE WE SHOULD JUST DECLARE **VICTORY** AND GET OUT! I'VE GOT A **PLAN**--

FORGET IT, RINO! IT'S **MY** WAY OR THE NON-FEDERALLY-FUNDED **HIGHWAY!**

YOU ARE ON THE VERGE OF ALMOST ANNOYING ME.

WILL MIDDLE-MAN OFFER **ENOUGH**? WILL HIS ARCH-RIVALS ACCEPT **SLIGHTLY LESS** THAN THEY WOULD HAVE **PREFERRED**? AND--WHAT HAPPENS AFTER **THAT**??

WE TRIED TO **SAVE** THE ENTITLEMENTS YOU RELY ON--BUT **MIDDLE-MAN** INSISTED THAT THEY HAD TO BE **SLASHED!**

THE CALLOUS **FIEND!**

GASP! WHO COULD HAVE FORESEEN **THIS**?

LIVE VIDEO FEED

UNDOUBTEDLY TO BE **CONTINUED!**

THIS MODERN WORLD

by TOM TOMORROW

Panel 1:
SO YOU MAY HAVE READ ABOUT SOME LITTLE SO-CALLED PHONE HACKING SCANDAL IN BRITAIN.

APPARENTLY A *FEW BAD APPLES* EMPLOYED BY RUPERT MURDOCH WERE SOMEWHAT OVERZEALOUS IN THEIR NEWS-GATHERING TECHNIQUES.

Panel 2:
MR. MURDOCH KNEW NOTHING ABOUT ANY OF THIS! OBVIOUSLY HE CAN'T BE EXPECTED TO KEEP TRACK OF *EVERY TINY DETAIL* OF HIS ENORMOUS MEDIA EMPIRE!

HE PROBABLY DOESN'T KNOW WHEN THE EMPLOYEE BREAK ROOM NEEDS *COFFEE FILTERS*, EITHER! HA HA!

HA HA!

Panel 3:
AND IT GOES WITHOUT SAYING THAT *FOX NEWS* IS IN NO WAY IMPLICATED IN THE ALLEGED SCANDAL.

NO ONE AT *THIS* NETWORK WOULD *EVER* HACK INTO SOMEONE'S VOICEMAIL IN PURSUIT OF A NEWS STORY--

Panel 4:
--BECAUSE *WE'RE NOT A NEWS ORGANIZATION!* I MEAN, SERIOUSLY--HAVE YOU EVER *WATCHED* THIS CHANNEL?

WE DON'T REPORT *NEWS!* WE JUST MAKE CRAP *UP!*

EVERYBODY KNOWS *THAT!*

Panel 5:
COUGH

Panel 6:
COMING UP *NEXT:* BRUTAL HEAT WAVE PROVES GLOBAL WARMING IS A *HOAX*, ACCORDING TO STATISTICS I JUST PULLED OUT OF MY BUTT!

AND--DOES VOTING FOR DEMOCRATS CAUSE *CANCER?* WHO *KNOWS!* IT *MIGHT!*

IT'S CERTAINLY FOOD FOR *THOUGHT!*

FIRST THESE *MESSAGES...*

TOM TOMORROW ©2011 ...www.thismodernworld.com....twitter.com/tomtomorrow

THIS MODERN WORLD

by TOM TOMORROW

From the files of...

THOMAS FRIEDMAN, PRIVATE EYE

I WAS IN MY OFFICE THINKING UP PITHY NEW **METAPHORS** WHEN A DISTRAUGHT-LOOKING MAN BURST IN...

THE POLITICAL PROCESS IS LIKE A DINER WITH ONLY ONE THING ON THE MENU--**BALONEY SAND-WICHES!** AND IT'S CALLED THE "TOO MUCH BALONEY DINER"!

GET IT? "TOO MUCH **BALONEY**?"

MISTER FRIED-MAN--I NEED YOUR **HELP!**

YOU SEE, WHEN I UNLOCKED MY OFFICE THIS MORNING, I REALIZED SOMETHING WAS **MISSING**--

YOU MEAN A **VIABLE THIRD PARTY** WHOSE CENTRIST POL-ITICS EXACTLY MIRROR MY **OWN**?

I'M **ON** IT!

ER--THAT'S NOT--

I RUSHED OUT TO CONSULT WITH ONE OF MY USUAL **SOURCES**...

TELL ME, DRIVER--DO YOU SENSE A WIDESPREAD THOUGH UNARTICULATED YEARNING FOR A SELF-STYLED POST-PARTISAN LEADER WHO VALUES COMPROMISE FOR THE SAKE OF COMPROMISE ABOVE **ALL ELSE**?

UH, WELL--DOESN'T THAT DESCRIBE THE PRESIDENT WE AL-READY **HAVE**?

I'LL JUST PUT YOU DOWN AS A "YES."

TAXI

NEXT, I RACED TO THE SWANKY OFFICES OF A **HEDGE FUND MANAGER** I KNEW!

THE **REAL** PROBLEM WITH POLITICS IS ALL THE **DISAGREEMENT!** IF POLITICIANS WOULD STOP **ARGUING**, THEY COULD WORK TOGETHER--TO GET THINGS **DONE**!

DOESN'T MATTER **WHAT**! JUST, YOU KNOW--**THINGS**!

I COULDN'T HAVE SAID IT MORE ASTUTELY MYSELF!

SO IN LIEU OF AN ACTUAL GRASS-ROOTS MOVEMENT--**I'M** FINANCING A **WEBSITE**!

THE TRANSFORMATIVE POWER OF THE INTERNET WILL TRANS-FORM **POLITICS**! LOOK OUT, BIG CHANGING ROBOT GUYS FROM THOSE POPULAR MOVIES--THERE'S A **NEW** TRANSFORMER IN TOWN! AM I **RIGHT**?

UH--SURE, TOM. WHAT-EVER YOU SAY.

WHEN I GOT BACK TO THE OFFICE, MY CLIENT WAS **GONE**...BUT BE-FORE **LONG**--

MISTER FRIEDMAN--I HAVE A **PROBLEM**--

--THE LACK OF A THIRD PARTY WHOSE CENTRIST POLITICS PRECISELY MIRROR MY **OWN**?

NOT TO WORRY--I'M **ALREADY ON THE CASE!**

THIS MODERN WORLD

by TOM TOMORROW

THE MODERATELY EXCITING ADVENTURES OF
MIDDLE MAN

MODERN COMICS GROUP
12¢

IF THEY BRING A **KNIFE** TO THE FIGHT--

--**I** BRING A **REASONABLE BIPARTISAN COMPROMISE!**

THIS WEEK: DEBTPOCALYPSE **DEFERRED!**

OUR HERO AND HIS ESTEEMED ARCH-RIVAL HAVE JUST SURVIVED A **BRUISING** BATTLE...

I HAD **HOPED** TO USE THIS OC-CASION TO REACH A **GRAND BAR-GAIN**--BUT YOUR SIDE'S RELUCTANCE TO ACCEPT MY PRE-EMPTIVE COM-PROMISES PROVED **MOST** VEXING!

WHAT CHANCE DID **EITHER** OF US HAVE--AGAINST THE AWESOME POWER OF THE **TEA PARTY?**

TRUE ENOUGH! BUT IN THE END, WE ARRIVED AT A **VERY** REA-SONABLE SOLUTION--

--A BIPARTISAN **SUPER-COM-MITTEE** WHICH **MUST** ACHIEVE COMPROMISE--LEST THEY TRIGGER DRACONIAN CUTS IN BOTH DEFENSE AND DOMESTIC SPENDING!

BUT NOT, OF COURSE, TAX INCREASES.

THERE **ARE** LIMITS TO COMPROMISE.

SUDDENLY--IN BURSTS THE ONE VILLAIN WITH WHOM MIDDLE-MAN WILL **NEVER** COMPROMISE--THE **DISSATISFIED LEFTIST!**

SERIOUSLY, MIDDLE-MAN? THE G.O.P. WAS READY TO DRIVE THE ECONOMY INTO A DITCH RATHER THAN MAKE THE **SLIGHTEST** CONCESSION ON REVENUE--

--AND NOW YOU'RE BETTING EVERY-THING ON THEIR WILLINGNESS TO COMPROMISE **NEXT** TIME? ARE YOU **KIDDING** ME??

DO YOU HEAR A VAGUE WHINING SOUND, AS IF AN UNSEEN **INSECT** HAS SOMEHOW GAINED ACCESS TO THE ROOM?

NO. NO, I REALLY DO NOT.

RIGHT. ME NEITHER.

SIGH.

NEXT TIME: SUPER-COMMITTEE **STALEMATE!**

NO ONE COULD HAVE--

--OH, YOU KNOW.

TOM TOMORROW ©2011 ...www.thismodernworld.com...twitter.com/tomtomorrow

52

THIS MODERN WORLD

by TOM TOMORROW

the story of...

Tea Party Tim...

...and Plutocrat Pete!

TWO YEARS AGO: AN UNLIKELY FRIENDSHIP IS BORN!

TAXES *SUCK!* WE OUGHTA DROWN GOVERNMENT IN A *BATHTUB!*

BY JOVE! I LIKE THE CUT OF YOUR JIB!

BUT MORE RECENTLY--

WE *CAN'T* LET THEM RAISE THE DEBT CEILING! WE'VE GOT TOO MUCH DEBT *ALREADY!* RIGHT, PLUTOCRAT PETE?

ER--WELL--THAT'S NOT *PRECISELY* HOW IT WORKS--

AND THEN--

NEXT TIME WE'LL FORCE 'EM TO *DEFAULT!* IT'S THE *ONLY WAY* TO GET SPENDING UNDER CONTROL!

DEAR LORD-- YOU'RE *SERIOUS!*

I THOUGHT YOUR UNINFORMED OUTRAGE WOULD BE USEFUL IN MY ETERNAL STRUGGLE TO AVOID TAXATION! I DIDN'T REALIZE YOU WERE A NIHILISTIC *MORON* WILLING TO CRASH THE ENTIRE *ECONOMY!*

IF YOU'LL *EXCUSE* ME, I'VE GOT TO GO TRANSFER SOME ASSETS INTO U.S. TREASURY BONDS--WHERE THEY'LL BE *SAFE!*

HARRUMPH!

THEN CAN WE DROWN GOVERNMENT IN THE BATHTUB?

THIS MODERN WORLD

by TOM TOMORROW

--AND IT'S TIME ONCE AGAIN FOR **POINTLESS SPECULATION** ABOUT THE 2012 **PRESIDENTIAL CAMPAIGN!**

ELECTION DAY **IS** A MERE YEAR AND A HALF AWAY!

440 DAYS, TO BE **PRECISE!**

MITT ROMNEY IS THE OBVIOUS MEDIA-ANNOINTED FRONT-RUNNER IN THE G.O.P. RACE AT THIS MOMENT--

--BUT MICHELE BACHMANN **DID** MAKE A STRONG SHOWING AMONG A STATISTICALLY MEANINGLESS SAMPLING OF IOWA STRAW POLL VOTERS!

WELL, SHE **IS** THE ONLY CANDIDATE PROMISING **TWO DOLLAR A GALLON** GAS IF SHE WINS!*

YES--BUT NOW THAT **RICK PERRY** HAS THROWN **HIS** COWBOY HAT IN THE RING, ALL BETS ARE **OFF!**

*SERIOUSLY, SHE SAYS THAT.

WITH HIS STRAIGHT TALK AND TEXAS SWAGGER, PERRY HAS MADE **QUITE AN IMPRESSION** ON COMMENTATORS SUCH AS OURSELVES!

HE **IS** A STRONG CONTENDER TO THE BE THE **NEXT** MEDIA-ANNOINTED FRONT-RUNNER, IF HE CAN REFRAIN FROM THREATENING BODILY HARM TO ANY MORE GOVERNMENT OFFICIALS!

AND NOW FOR A QUICK RECAP OF THE DAY'S **OTHER** NEWS!

WAR, FAMINE, RIOTS, ECONOMIC CALAMITY, MURDER, MAYHEM AND DESPAIR!

YADDA, YADDA YADDA, BLAH BLAH BLAH!

NOW LET'S GET BACK TO THE **IMPORTANT** QUESTION--

--**WHO** WILL WIN THE REPUBLICAN NOMINATION NEXT SUMMER?

ACCORDING TO **MY** LATEST GUT FEELING, IT COULD BE **PERRY**--UNLESS IT'S **ROMNEY** OR **BACHMANN!**

OR MAYBE CHRISTIE OR RYAN.

WE'LL HAVE **MORE** SPECULATION--AFTER THESE MESSAGES!

FOR THE NEXT 10,605 HOURS, GIVE OR TAKE.

BEATS WORKING.

THIS MODERN WORLD

by TOM TOMORROW

Panel 1:

THIS WEEK: ANOTHER MYSTERY FROM THE CASEFILES OF *CONSERVATIVE JONES, BOY DETECTIVE!*

COME IN, MOONBAT! YOU'RE JUST IN TIME! I AM ATTEMPTING TO SOLVE THE ENIGMA OF *RECENT LIBERAL BEHAVIOR!*

OH, THIS SHOULD BE GOOD.

Panel 2:

FOR *INSTANCE*--WHEN ERIC CANTOR QUITE REASONABLY SUGGESTS THAT DISASTER RELIEF SHOULD BE CONTINGENT UPON *BUDGET CUTS*--WHY DO LIBERALS *OBJECT*?

UM--BECAUSE IT IS HEARTLESS AND TONE DEAF?

OH, MOONBAT! HOW I *ENVY* YOUR BLISSFUL DETATCHMENT FROM REALITY!

Panel 3:

BUT TO *CONTINUE*--THE MYSTERY IS *COMPOUNDED* BY THE LEFT'S RESPONSE TO *RON PAUL*--WHO SIMPLY POINTED OUT THAT THEY DIDN'T NEED *FEMA* DURING THE GREAT HURRICANE OF 1900!

YOU MEAN WHEN THOUSANDS DIED AND MEN WERE CONSCRIPTED TO BURN THE CORPSES PILED UP ROTTING ON THE BEACHES OF GALVESTON?

Panel 4:

MOONBAT, YOUR FLAIR FOR THE *DRAMATIC* IS MATCHED ONLY BY THE SLAVISHNESS OF YOUR DEVOTION TO GOVERNMENT *SPENDING!* WHICH BRINGS US TO OUR *FINAL* DATA POINT--

--THE INEXPLICABLE LIBERAL RESISTANCE TO SIMPLY *DEFUNDING* THE *NATIONAL WEATHER SERVICE!*

Panel 5:

AFTER ALL--WHY *SHOULD* TAXPAYERS BE FORCED TO FOOT THE BILL FOR A SERVICE WHICH PRIVATE SECTOR COMPANIES SUCH AS *ACCUWEATHER* CAN PROVIDE?

BUT--THOSE COMPANIES USE N.W.S. DATA--!

QUIET, MOONBAT! THROUGH A RIGOROUS PROCESS OF DEDUCTION, I HAVE ARRIVED AT THE *SOLUTION*--

Panel 6:

--AND IT IS THAT...*LIBERALS* ARE JUST *IRRATIONAL!*

BY GOD, I'VE DONE IT *AGAIN!*

I'LL ALERT THE MEDIA.

NEXT: *WHY* ARE LIBERALS SO OBSESSED WITH *GLOBAL WARMING*? THEY *IGNORE* EXPERTS SUCH AS *RUSH LIMBAUGH!* IT MAKES NO *SENSE!*

TOM TOMORROW ©2011 ...www.thismodernworld.com...twitter.com/tomtomorrow

THIS MODERN WORLD

by TOM TOMORROW

Panel 1:
GREETINGS! IS THIS THE NATION-STATE KNOWN COLLOQUIALLY AS "YOU-ESS-AY," ON THE PLANET LOCALLY DESIGNATED AS "URTH"?

ER, YES--I SUPPOSE IT IS!

Panel 2:
EXCELLENT! AFTER YEARS OF STUDYING YOUR SOCIETY FROM AFAR, MY PEOPLE HAVE SENT ME TO OBSERVE FIRSTHAND THE PROCESS BY WHICH YOU SELECT A NEW *LEADER!*

Panel 3:
AS I UNDERSTAND IT, THE IDEOLOGICAL-SLASH-TRIBAL GROUPING KNOWN AS THE "REPUBLICANS" ARE CURRENTLY ENGAGED IN A SERIES OF VERBAL *JOUSTING MATCHES*--

--IN ORDER TO SELECT *THEIR* CHAMPION FOR THE FORTHCOMING RITUALIZED STRUGGLE FOR IDEOLOGICAL *DOMINANCE!*

UM, WELL--MORE OR LESS--

Panel 4:
VERY GOOD! I CANNOT *WAIT* TO OBSERVE THE SOMBER AND THOUGHTFUL PROCESS BY WHICH THE WISEST AND MOST KNOWLEDGABLE AMONG YOU VIE FOR THE ULTIMATE HONOR AND RESPONSIBILITY OF RULING YOUR NATION-STATE!

WHAT AN INFORMED AND ENGAGED CITIZENRY YOU MUST HAVE! ONCE I FILE MY REPORT, I EXPECT YOU WILL SERVE AS AN INSPIRATION THROUGHOUT THE *GALAXY!*

Panel 5:
(no dialogue)

Panel 6:
YOU HAVEN'T BEEN STUDYING US *TOO* CLOSELY, I TAKE IT.

ENOUGH CHATTER, EARTHLING! SHOW ME THE FINEST YOUR CIVILIZATION HAS TO OFFER!

TAKE ME TO YOUR WOULD-BE *LEADERS!*

THIS MODERN WORLD

by TOM TOMORROW

TEA PARTY NIHILISTS

ANOTHER IN AN OCCASIONAL SERIES OF PARABLES INVOLVING CLIFFS

LOOK OUT! YOU'RE HEADED STRAIGHT FOR THAT **CLIFF!**

INDEED **I AM!**

WELL FOR GOD'S SAKE--SLOW DOWN BEFORE YOU CRASH THE **CAR!**

ACTUALLY I'M SICK OF THIS CAR. THE PASSENGER DOOR STICKS AND THE CUPHOLDERS ARE TOO SMALL. AND I HAVE TO PAY **TAXES** EVERY TIME I FILL THE TANK!

BUT--THAT'S NO REASON TO DRIVE US OVER A **CLIFF!**

I WOULDN'T EXPECT A LAMESTREAM ELITIST LIKE YOU TO UNDER- STAND.

AIIIEEEEEEEEEEEEE

OKAY, YOU GOT MY ATTENTION. NOW WHAT?

HECK IF **I** KNOW. I WAS COUNTING ON YOU TO STOP ME BEFORE I DID ANYTHING STUPID.

TOM TOMORROW © 2011 ...www.thismodernworld.com...twitter.com/tomtomorrow

THIS MODERN WORLD

by TOM TOMORROW

MIDDLE MAN
THIS WEEK: OUR STORY SO FAR!

Panel 1:
TIME AND AGAIN, MIDDLE-MAN REACHES OUT TO HIS ESTEEMED ARCH-RIVALS.

HELLO, THIS IS *MIDDLE-MAN* CALLING FOR CAPTAIN ORANGE! I HAVE AN IMPORTANT *PROPOSAL*--

ER--THAT'S M-I-D-D-L-E-M-A-N.

YES, I'LL HOLD.

Panel 2:
TIME AND AGAIN, HE IS REBUFFED.

I'M *SURE* WE CAN SET ASIDE OUR DIFFERENCES--AND WORK TO-GETHER TO ACHIEVE A *BIPARTI-SAN COMPROMISE!*

WE *TOTALLY* AGREE--

--*NOT!!*

JOINK!

Panel 3:
AFTER THREE YEARS, HE SUDDENLY REALIZES SOMETHING IS *AMISS!*

IT'S--IT'S AS IF THEY NEVER HAD ANY *INTENTION* OF COMPROMISING!

Panel 4:
AND SO HE TRIES SOMETHING *NEW*.

I AM *ABANDONING* THE AWE-SOME POWER OF THE PRE-EMPTIVE COMPROMISE! *THIS* TIME, TO USE THE POPULAR COLLOQUIALISM, IT'S *MY* WAY--OR THE, UH, FEDERAL INTERSTATE SYSTEM!

DID I GET THAT RIGHT?

I'M NEW AT THIS.

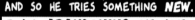

Panel 5:
AND THEN HIS STRUGGLE *REALLY* BEGINS.

OH, MIDDLE-MAN--WE'D LIKE TO REQUEST SOME MINOR *CONCES-SIONS!* DON'T YOU WANT TO MEET US *HALFWAY?*

YOU KNOW-- FIND A *COM-PROMISE?*

MUST...BE... *STRONG...* MUST NOT... GIVE...*IN!*

CAN MIDDLE-MAN *RESIST* THEIR SIREN SONG? STAY TUNED FOR *MORE* PULSE-POUNDING SUSPENSE!

Panel 6:
ALSO COMING UP: TEARS OF THE *PUNDIT!*

I THOUGHT MIDDLE-MAN WAS A *DIF-FERENT* SORT OF DEM-OCRAT--ONE WHO AGREED WITH *ME!*

I HAZ A *SAD!*

Panel 7:
AND: THE IMPLAUSIBLE MENACE OF *CRAZY TEXAS BIBLE MAN!*

GLOBAL WARMING IS A *HOAX!*

SOCIAL SECURITY IS A *SCAM!*

PRAY FOR *RAIN*--

--AND PASS THE *AMMU-NITION!*

THIS MODERN WORLD

by TOM TOMORROW

TOP REPUBLICANS CONSULT WITH THE BRILLIANT DR. VON PHILBERT!

WE WANT TO GIVE AMERICANS *LOWER GAS PRICES!*

PREFERABLY IN THE $2 A GALLON RANGE!

NO PROBLEM! I HAVE A SIMPLE PLAN!

USING MY NEWLY-COMPLETED *TIME TUNNEL*, I WILL SEND YOU MILLIONS OF YEARS INTO THE PAST—TO THE LAND MASS WHICH WILL EVENTUALLY BECOME THE U.S.—

—WHERE YOU WILL EXPONENTIALLY INCREASE THE *DINOSAUR POPULATION* THROUGH A PROCESS OF ACCELERATED *CLONING!*

YOU WILL *THEN* HUNT THEM DOWN AND *KILL* THEM! BY THE TIME YOU RETURN, THERE WILL BE PLENTY OF EXTRA OIL—RIGHT UNDER OUR OWN *FEET!*

BUT YOU MUST BE VERY CAREFUL NOT TO CHANGE ANYTHING *ELSE* IN THE PAST.

ALL RIGHT—LET'S *DO* IT!

LOCK AND *LOAD!*

EVERYTHING SEEMS TO GO ACCORDING TO *PLAN...*

...AND SOON, THE TRAVELERS RETURN. DID IT *WORK?* WERE WE *SUCCESSFUL?*

WELL, FUNNY STORY. IT LOOKS LIKE I ACCIDENTALLY SENT YOU TO WHAT IS NOW *VENEZUELA*—SO *HUGO CHAVEZ* NOW HAS *PLENTY* OF EXTRA OIL THANKS TO YOU...

D'OH!

OH, AND IN THIS TIMELINE, *BARACK OBAMA* WON THE ELECTION IN 2008, RATHER THAN PRESIDENT MᶜCAIN.

ONE OF YOU MUST HAVE STEPPED ON A BUTTERFLY OR SOMETHING.

OH MY *GOD*—WHAT HAVE WE *DONE?*

EWW—WHAT'S THIS THING ON MY *BOOT?*

THIS MODERN WORLD

by TOM TOMORROW

SO WHAT DO THESE WALL STREET PROTESTERS **WANT**, ANYWAY?

HECK IF **I** KNOW! BUT MAYBE WE CAN GET SOME ANSWERS FROM OUR NEXT GUEST--

--AN **ACTUAL WALL STREET DEMONSTRATOR!** TELL ME, SIR--WHAT, EXACTLY, ARE YOU **PROTESTING**?

ECONOMIC INJUSTICE.

SORRY, WHAT WAS THAT?

ECONOMIC INJUSTICE.

STILL NOT GETTING IT.

ECONOMIC INJUSTICE! WE ARE PROTESTING **ECONOMIC INJUSTICE!**

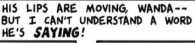

HIS LIPS ARE MOVING, WANDA-- BUT I CAN'T UNDERSTAND A WORD HE'S **SAYING!**

IS THAT EVEN **ENGLISH**-- OR JUST RANDOM **GIBBERISH**?

ECONOMIC INJUSTICE!

E-CO-NO-MIC--IN-JUS-TICE--

WELL, HE CERTAINLY SEEMED TO BE WORKED UP ABOUT **SOMETHING!**

HARD TO KNOW **WHAT!**

IT'S A MYSTERY TO **ME!**

OKAY THEN! COMING UP NEXT-- ARE THE PROTESTERS FRIVOLOUS **NINNIES** WHO JUST WANT TO PLAY **BONGO DRUMS** AND SMOKE **MARIJUANA**?*

IN WHICH CASE, WHY DON'T THEY #OCCUPY-A-BEATNIK-COFFEE-SHOP-IN-1957?

ALSO: WHAT DO OUR FRIENDS IN THE **TEA PARTY** THINK?

FIRST THESE MESSAGES.

*AS SUGGESTED BY CNN'S ALISON KOSIK

THIS MODERN WORLD

by TOM TOMORROW

INVISIBLE-HAND-OF-THE-FREE-MARKET-MAN vs. THE OCCUPATION!

IF YOU'RE INVISIBLE, WHY ARE YOUR FLAWS SO READILY APPARENT?

SHOULDN'T YOU BE AT A DRUM CIRCLE OR SOMETHING?

WE ARE THE 99%

IN A DOWNTOWN SKYSCRAPER, BE-SIEGED BANKERS HUDDLE TOGETHER FOR **SECURITY!**

THEY'RE STILL DOWN THERE--AND THEY'RE STILL SAYING **MEAN THINGS** ABOUT US!

I HAVEN'T BEEN SO HURT SINCE **OBAMA** WAS MILDLY CRITICAL OF US!

DON'T THEY UNDERSTAND THAT WE HAVE FEELINGS **TOO**?

SUDDENLY--

FEAR NOT, HARD-WORKING JOB CREATORS! IT IS **I**--YOUR HUMBLE **SERVANT!**

INVISIBLE-HAND-OF-THE-FREE-MARKET-MAN! YOU'RE THE ONLY ONE WHO CAN **SAVE** US!

NOT TO MEN-TION THE BESMIRCHED HONOR OF **CAPITALISM ITSELF!**

SO, HERE'S MY PLAN...WITH THE HELP OF CERTAIN COMPLIANT CON-SERVATIVE PUNDITS, WE'LL PAINT THE PROTESTERS AS **MILQUE-TOASTS** WITH **SMALL IDEAS**--

--WHILE PORTRAYING AUSTERITY HAWKS WHO WANT TO CUT SOCIAL SECURITY AS THE **TRUE** VISIONARIES!

SORRY, DID YOU JUST USE THE WORD "MILQUETOASTS"?

YES. YES, I DID.

MEANWHILE, WE'LL PROMOTE STORIES OF POVERTY-STRICKEN, DEBT-RIDDLED AMERICANS WITH NO HEALTH IN-SURANCE WHO ARE **HAPPY** TO MAKE DO WITH LESS--

--SO THAT WEALTH PRODUCERS SUCH AS YOURSELVES CAN BE REWARDED WITH **EVEN MORE!**

WELL, IT ALL SOUNDS PERFECTLY CONVINCING TO **ME!**

HOW COULD ANYONE **FAIL** TO BE PER-SUADED BY SUCH COMPELLING AR-GUMENTS?

BY **JOVE**, HAND-- YOU'VE DONE IT **AGAIN!**

NEXT: AN UNANTICIPATED DEVELOPMENT!

WHAT ARE THEY **LAUGH-ING** AT?

I--I DON'T **KNOW**...

TOM TOMORROW © 2011 ...www.thismodernworld.com...twitter.com/tomtomorrow

61

THIS MODERN WORLD

by TOM TOMORROW

BREAKING NEWS: POVERTY ELIMINATED

WE TURN NOW TO AN EXCLUSIVE ACTION McNEWS **NEWS McBULLETIN!**

WE'VE JUST RECEIVED WORD THAT THERE IS **NO MORE POVERTY** IN **AMERICA!**

FOR MORE ON THIS DEVELOPING STORY, WE GO LIVE TO OUR REPORTER ON THE SCENE, **BETTY McBETTIE!** BETTY?

THANKS BIFF! I'M STANDING IN ONE OF OUR CITY'S PURPORTEDLY LOW-INCOME NEIGHBORHOODS, WHERE A FEW SHORT MINUTES AGO, I WITNESSED AN ALLEGEDLY "POOR" PERSON--

--USING A **CELLULAR TELEPHONE!**

I ASK YOU-- HOW CAN SOMEONE WHO SUPPOSEDLY HAS NO MONEY AFFORD A LUXURY LIKE **THAT?**

NOW JUST TO BE SURE, I FOLLOWED HIM HOME AND PEERED IN THROUGH HIS WINDOWS, WHERE I OBSERVED THAT HE HAS BOTH **KITCHEN APPLIANCES,** AND-- AS YOU CAN SEE BEHIND ME-- A **WORKING TELEVISION!**

SINCE THESE THINGS WOULD CONSTITUTE UNPARALLELED **RICHES** IN MANY THIRD-WORLD NATIONS, THE CONCLUSION IS INESCAPABLE-- POVERTY IN **THIS** COUNTRY HAS BEEN **VASTLY** OVERSTATED!

BACK TO YOU, BIFF AND WANDA!

THANKS, BETTY! WELL, WANDA, IT'S LIKE I ALWAYS SUSPECTED--UNLESS YOU ARE LITERALLY LIVING IN A CARDBOARD BOX, YOU HAVE **NOTHING** TO COMPLAIN ABOUT!

AND IF YOU **ARE** LIVING IN A BOX, IT'S UNDOUBTEDLY YOUR OWN FAULT, SO YOU STILL CAN'T COMPLAIN.

SUCK IT UP WHINERS!

WE'LL BE BACK AFTER THESE MESSAGES.

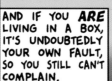

THIS MODERN WORLD

by TOM TOMORROW

Panel 1:

HELLO, OFFICER FRIENDLY! ARE YOU HERE TO "PROTECT AND SERVE"?

YOU **BET** I AM! THAT'S WHAT THE POLICE ARE **FOR**, YOU KNOW!

Panel 2:

SO WHY DID THE OFFICER AT THE OCCUPY DEMONSTRATION IN NEW YORK MACE THE FLEEING WOMEN WHO CLEARLY POSED NO THREAT TO HIM OR ANYONE **ELSE**?

WE SAW IT ON THE INTERNET.

WELL, THAT'S **DIFFERENT**, SON! THOSE WERE **HIPPIES**!

Panel 3:

AND WHAT ABOUT THE POLICE AT THE OCCUPY PROTEST IN **OAKLAND**, WHO SHOT AN IRAQ WAR VET IN THE FACE WITH A "NONLETHAL PROJECTILE"--

--FRACTURING HIS **SKULL**--

Panel 4:

--AND THEN TOSSED A FLASH-BANG **GRENADE** INTO THE MIDDLE OF A CROWD OF PEOPLE TRYING TO HELP HIM AS HE LAY BLEEDING IN THE **STREET**?

THERE'S VIDEO OF **THAT** ONLINE AS WELL!

Panel 5:

Panel 6:

YOU KNOW, I THINK THIS COULD EASILY QUALIFY AS AN "UNLAWFUL ASSEMBLY."

SOMETIMES YOU SCARE ME, OFFICER FRIENDLY.

WELCOME TO THE REAL WORLD, KID.

TOM TOMORROW © 2011 ... www.thismodernworld.com...twitter.com/tomtomorrow

THIS MODERN WORLD

by TOM TOMORROW

Panel 1:

IT'S TIME ONCE AGAIN TO CHECK IN ON *PARALLEL EARTH*--WHERE, AS ON OUR WORLD, REPUBLICANS SEEM *UNENTHUSED* ABOUT THEIR PRESIDENTIAL FIELD...

PATHETIC FOOLS! YOU CANNOT *BE-GIN* TO COMPREHEND MY GENIUS!

9-9-9!

6-6-6!

PLEASE DON'T GOOGLE ME.

Panel 2:

PARALLEL MITT ROMNEY IS VIEWED WITH SUSPICION BECAUSE HE ONCE DID SOMETHING RELATIVELY *SANE*...

HOW CAN WE VOTE FOR SOMEONE WHO ONCE SUPPORTED HEALTH CARE FOR THE *UNINSURED*?

A *REAL* REPUBLICAN WOULD REFUSE TO EVEN *ACKNOWLEDGE* THE PROBLEM!

THOUGH ON THE PLUS SIDE, HE *DOES* HAVE VERY PRESIDENTIAL *HAIR*!

Panel 3:

...WHILE THE GOVERNOR OF PARALLEL TEXAS HAS PROVEN TO BE SOMEWHAT LESS IMPRESSIVE THAN G.O.P. VOTERS MIGHT HAVE HOPED.

MY TAX FORM IS SO SHORT THAT IT'S LIKE, IT WAS LONGER BEFORE IT, YOU KNOW, FROM THE STANDPOINT OF, UM, SHORTER AND LONGER, IT'S, I MEAN, YOU KNOW--

OH WOW, WHERE WAS I?

TAXES

Panel 4:

AND THEN THERE'S THE QUESTION OF *PARALLEL HERMAN CAIN.*

WILL THE PRETEND CANDIDACY OF THE MAN WHO NEVER HAD A REMOTE *CHANCE* OF WINNING THE NOMINATION LET ALONE THE PRESIDENCY BE *DERAILED* BY THE SEXUAL HARASSMENT SCANDAL?

OR WILL THE INEXPLICABLE CHARADE OF HIS CAMPAIGN SURVIVE A FEW MONTHS *LONGER*?

llel on ews ork

Parallel Action McNews Network

P· A Mc Ne

Panel 5:

HOWEVER...THERE IS ONE SMALL BUT CRUCIAL DIFFERENCE BETWEEN THE REPUBLICAN FIELD OF PARALLEL EARTH AND OUR OWN...ONE ADDITIONAL CANDIDATE WHO MIGHT PROVE *IRRESISTIBLE* TO PARALLEL REPUBLICAN VOTERS...

Panel 6:

...AN *ACTUAL NEANDERTHAL* NAMED UGG!

AND BY "ACTUAL" WE MEAN "AS COMMONLY PORTRAYED IN CONTEMPORARY POPULAR CULTURE."

UGG *SMASH* NEXT BIG-BRAIN WHO SAY UGG NOT *REAL* NEANDERTHAL!

UGG *TIRED* OF PEDANTRY!

SENIOR CAMPAIGN ADVISOR--DR. VON PHILBERT!

Panel 7:

NEXT: THE PARALLEL RACE HEATS *UP*!

UGG REPRESENTS A RETURN TO *REALLY* TRADITIONAL VALUES!

AND HE PROMISES TO SMASH OUR ENEMIES!

THIS MODERN WORLD

by TOM TOMORROW

Panel 1:
CONTRARY TO POPULAR BELIEF, G.O.P. VOTERS KNOW *EXACTLY* WHO THEY WANT--AND IT IS--

NOT MITT ROMNEY

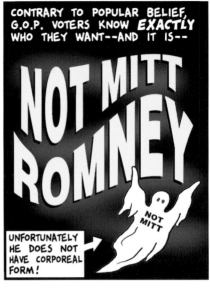

NOT MITT

UNFORTUNATELY HE DOES NOT HAVE CORPOREAL FORM!

Panel 2:
HE BRIEFLY INHABITED THE BODY OF *DONALD TRUMP*...

I AM *NOT MITT ROMNEY!*

ALSO OBAMA IS A KENYAN.

...BUT THAT DIDN'T LAST LONG.

Panel 3:
HE THEN MOVED ON TO *MICHELE BACHMANN*...

I--I AM NOT MITT ROMNEY!

AND VACCINES MAKE YOU RETARDED.

?!

...BUT SHE ALSO BURNED OUT QUICKLY.

Panel 4:
THE ETHEREAL CANDIDATE THEN TOOK POSSESSION OF *RICK PERRY*...

I WAS NOT MITT ROMNEY BEFORE MITT ROMNEY WAS FOR THE, UM, THING HE WAS AGAINST--

ER--I MEAN--

OOPS.

...BUT FOUND HIS SPEECH CENTER TOO DIFFICULT TO CONTROL.

Panel 5:
HERMAN CAIN *SEEMED* TO PROVIDE A PROMISING HOST BODY...

FOR EVERY WOMAN WHO SAYS HERMAN CAIN HARASSED HER--

--THERE ARE *999* WHO SAY HE *DIDN'T!*

...BUT HE TURNED OUT TO HAVE A LITTLE TOO MUCH BAGGAGE.

Panel 6:
WHILE NOT MITT IS SAID TO BE EYEING *NEWT GINGRICH* NEXT, IT'S NOT HARD TO PREDICT WHERE HE'LL *ULTIMATELY* END UP...

I AM *NOT MITT ROMNEY!!*

JEEZ! WHAT A *FLIP-FLOPPER!*

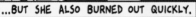

TOM TOMORROW ©2011 ...www.thismodernworld.com... TIP O' THE PEN(GUIN) TO AL PETTERSON!

65

THIS MODERN WORLD

by TOM TOMORROW

Panel 1: LET'S FACE IT--"SEXUAL HARASSMENT" IS A *MYTH!*

ANYONE WHO CLAIMS OTHERWISE IS OBVIOUSLY A *LYING TROLLOP!*

Panel 2: IT'S JUST SOMETHING THE MAN-HATING FEMINISTS DREAMED UP TO MAKE THEMSELVES *RICH!*

THERE'S NO SURER PATH TO FAME AND FORTUNE!

Panel 3: I BET ALL THESE SO-CALLED ACCUSERS ARE SECRETLY HOPING TO BE THE NEXT *ANITA HILL!*

IT'S BEEN NOTHING BUT SMOOTH SAILING FOR *HER!*

Panel 4: AND IT GOES WITHOUT SAYING THAT THESE FEMINAZIS HAVE NO SENSE OF *HUMOR!*

WHAT IS THE WORLD COMING TO, WHEN YOU CAN'T EVEN JOKE WITH A FEMALE EMPLOYEE ABOUT THE SEX YOU'D LIKE TO HAVE WITH HER?

Panel 5: *AND* THEY DON'T KNOW HOW TO TAKE A *COMPLIMENT!*

IF A RESPECTABLE BUSINESSMAN HAPPENS TO FIND A YOUNG JOB APPLICANT SEXUALLY AROUSING-- WHAT'S THE HARM IN LETTING HER *KNOW*?

YOU'D *THINK* SHE'D BE *FLATTERED!*

Panel 6: NO QUESTION ABOUT IT--*MEN* ARE THE *REAL* VICTIMS HERE.

SOMETIMES I DON'T KNOW HOW WE FIND THE STRENGTH TO CARRY ON EACH DAY.

HEY HOT STUFF! NICE RACK!

PISS OFF.

OH, THE *HUMANITY!*

THIS MODERN WORLD

by TOM TOMORROW

SO YOU'RE SAYING PEOPLE WHO LOSE THEIR HOMES OR JOBS HAVE ONLY THEMSELVES TO BLAME?

EXACTLY! THEY SHOULD HAVE MADE *BETTER DECISIONS!*

AND IF SOMEONE GETS REALLY SICK AND DOESN'T HAVE HEALTH INSURANCE, OR HAS AN INSURANCE COMPANY THAT DENIES TREATMENT?

DON'T COME WHINING TO *ME!* MAYBE THEY CAN HOLD A *BAKE SALE* OR SOMETHING!

SO AS FAR AS YOU'RE CONCERNED, ANYONE WHO SUFFERS AN UNEXPECTED SETBACK IS BASICALLY ON THEIR *OWN?*

THAT'S WHAT FREEDOM IS *ABOUT!* THIS IS A COUNTRY OF *RUGGED INDIVIDUALISTS!* WE TAKE CARE OF *OURSELVES!* WE DON'T NEED--

1 ton

WHOOMP!

URK.

1 ton

WELL, THAT WAS A LITTLE HEAVY-HANDED, DON'T YOU THINK?

IT'S A SIX-PANEL CARTOON. WE DON'T HAVE A LOT OF ROOM FOR NUANCE.

NO PROBLEM... I GOT THIS...

I'LL JUST LIE HERE AND THINK ABOUT AYN RAND...

1 ton

THIS MODERN WORLD

by TOM TOMORROW

A BRIEF GUIDE TO CLASS CONFLICT IN AMERICA

THE COUNTRY IS FALLING APART.

--AND DUE TO BUDGET CUTS, THE CITY CANNOT AFFORD TO RESCUE THE LAID-OFF FORECLOSURE VICTIM FROM THE RUBBLE OF THE BRIDGE THAT JUST COLLAPSED DUE TO **PREVIOUS** BUDGET CUTS!

MAYBE SOMEONE CAN HOLD A **BAKE SALE!**

THE TOP ONE PERCENT CONTROL AN INCREASINGLY DISPROPORTIONATE SHARE OF THE WEALTH.

BUT DON'T EVEN **THINK** ABOUT RAISING **OUR** TAXES.

WE ARE SOCIETY'S **JOB CREATORS!**

HYPOTHETICALLY SPEAKING, OF COURSE.

SENSIBLE CENTRISTS THINK THE ANSWER IS **OBVIOUS!**

IN THIS NEW AGE OF AUSTERITY, **EVERYONE** HAS TO SHARE THE PAIN! WE'RE **ALL** GOING TO HAVE TO TIGHTEN OUR BELTS!

BY WHICH WE MOSTLY MEAN YOU.

"CHUCKLES" THE SENSIBLE WOODCHUCK!

BUT MANY AMERICANS FIND THEIR LOGIC UNPERSUASIVE.

THE BANKERS WHO CRASHED THE ECONOMY MADE **BILLIONS** FROM THEIR BAILOUTS! BUT YOU WANT **US** TO EMBRACE **AUSTERITY?**

I SUPPOSE **YOU** THINK WE SHOULD "RAISE TAXES" ON THE "RICH"?

WELL-- ACTUALLY--

CRAZY HIPPIES!

MEANWHILE OUR PLUTOCRATIC OVER-LORDS ARE APPARENTLY CONTENT TO WATCH AMERICA DEVOLVE INTO A DYS-FUNCTIONAL THIRD-WORLD **HELLHOLE.**

IN OTHER WORDS--A GREAT SOURCE OF **REALLY CHEAP LABOR!**

I **TOLD** YOU WE WERE JOB CREATORS!

WHAT HAPPENS **NEXT?** STAY **TUNED!** (NOT THAT YOU HAVE ANY CHOICE...)

TOM TOMORROW © 2011 ...www.thismodernworld.com...twitter.com/tomtomorrow

THIS MODERN WORLD

by TOM TOMORROW

FUN FACTS ABOUT NEWT GINGRICH

NOTE: QUOTATION MARKS DENOTE GENUINE QUOTES

VISITED FIRST WIFE IN HOSPITAL TO DISCUSS DIVORCE.* CURRENTLY TRYING TO OBFUSCATE STORY BY DISPUTING DETAILS.

I MOST CERTAINLY DID **NOT** HAVE A YELLOW LEGAL PAD!

*SHE LATER HAD TO SUE HIM FOR UNPAID CHILD SUPPORT.

IN A 1992 NOTE TO HIMSELF, WROTE: "GINGRICH--PRIMARY MISSION, ADVOCATE OF CIVILIZATION, DEFINER OF CIVILIZATION, TEACHER OF THE RULES OF CIVILIZATION, AROUSER OF THOSE WHO FAN CIVILIZATION...LEADER (POSSIBLY) OF THE CIVILIZING FORCES."

HAS ALSO REFERRED TO HIMSELF AS A "TRANSFORMATIONAL FIGURE."

IN '95, INDIGNATION OVER A SEAT ASSIGNMENT ON AIR FORCE ONE LED TO BUDGET IMPASSE WHICH SHUT DOWN GOVERNMENT.

A **DEFINER** OF **CIVILIZATION** DOES NOT SIT AT THE **BACK** OF THE PLANE!

ACCORDING TO A FORMER MISTRESS, PREFERRED ORAL SEX BECAUSE HE COULD THEN DENY HAVING SLEPT WITH HER. ALSO TOLD HER:

"IF YOU EVER TELL ANYONE ABOUT THIS, I WILL SAY YOU ARE **LYING!**"

LED PERSECUTION OF BILL CLINTON FOR EXTRAMARITAL AFFAIR WHILE HAVING AN EXTRAMARITAL AFFAIR.

"IT DOESN'T MATTER WHAT I **DO**--PEOPLE NEED TO HEAR WHAT I HAVE TO **SAY!**"

HAS SUBSEQUENTLY BLAMED HIS NUMEROUS AFFAIRS ON THE INTENSITY OF HIS LOVE FOR AMERICA.

"THERE'S NO QUESTION AT TIMES OF MY LIFE, PARTIALLY DRIVEN BY HOW PASSIONATELY I FELT ABOUT THIS COUNTRY... THINGS HAPPENED IN MY LIFE THAT WERE NOT APPROPRIATE."

WAS FIRST SPEAKER IN 208 YEARS TO BE DISCIPLINED BY HOUSE FOR ETHICAL WRONGDOING; PAID UNPRECEDENTED $300,000 PENALTY.

SEE? I **AM** A TRANSFORMATIONAL FIGURE!

BLAMED THE MURDER OF TWO CHILDREN BY THEIR MOTHER ON DEMOCRATS.

"(IT) VIVIDLY REMINDS EVERY AMERICAN HOW SICK THE SOCIETY IS GETTING...THE ONLY WAY YOU GET CHANGE IS TO VOTE **REPUBLICAN!**"

CLAIMS TO BE BAFFLED BY OUR CENTRIST, TECHNOCRATIC PRESIDENT.

"WHAT IF HE IS SO OUTSIDE OF OUR COMPREHENSION, THAT ONLY IF YOU UNDERSTAND KENYAN, ANTICOLONIAL BEHAVIOR, CAN YOU BEGIN TO PIECE TOGETHER (HIS ACTIONS)?"

IN 1996 MEMO PURPORTING TO RESPOND TO THE "PLAINTIVE PLEAS" OF CANDIDATES WHO WISHED THEY COULD "SPEAK LIKE NEWT," COMPILED LIST OF TERMS FOR G.O.P. TO USE IN DESCRIBING DEMOCRATS, INCLUDING: **ANTI-FLAG, ANTI-CHILD, ANTI-FAMILY, BIZARRE, PATHETIC, SICK** AND OF COURSE, **TRAITORS.**

ACCORDING TO A RECENT POLL, IOWA VOTERS CONSIDER HIM "MOST APT TO BRING REPUBLICANS AND DEMOCRATS TOGETHER."

WHAT? WHY IS EVERYONE **LAUGHING**?

BONUS FUN FACT: IN HIGH SCHOOL NEWT COULD NOT FIND A FOOTBALL HELMET THAT FIT BECAUSE HIS **HEAD WAS TOO BIG.**

TOM TOMORROW © 2011 ... www.thismodernworld.com...twitter.com/tomtomorrow

THIS MODERN WORLD

by TOM TOMORROW

2011
AN ADMITTEDLY INCOMPLETE AND UTTERLY SUBJECTIVE YEAR IN REVIEW
PART THE FIRST

MONTH OF JANUARY: SENSITIVE, CARING REPUBLICANS TRY TO REDEFINE *RAPE*.

IT DOESN'T COUNT UNLESS IT WAS *FORCIBLE!*

OTHERWISE YOU WERE ASKING FOR IT.

JAN. 8: REP. GIFFORDS SHOT, SIX OTHERS KILLED; USUAL GUN NUT CRAP COMMENCES.

GUN OWNERS ARE THE *REAL* VICTIMS TODAY!

JAN. 10: SOON-TO-BE-FORGOTTEN CRAZY PERSON GLENN BECK URGES SOON-TO-BE-FORGOTTEN SELF PROMOTER SARAH PALIN TO HIRE MORE SECURITY BECAUSE--

"--AN ATTEMPT ON YOU COULD BRING THE RE-PUBLIC DOWN!"

FEBRUARY: SOUTH DAKOTA LAWMAKERS CONSIDER BILL JUSTIFYING HOMICIDE IN DEFENSE OF A FETUS.

WE CALL IT THE "OPEN SEASON ON ABORTION DOCS" ACT!

HAPPY HUNTIN'!

(BILL IS LATER WITHDRAWN)

ALSO: HEAVY SNOWSTORMS GENERATE PREDICTABLE RESPONSE FROM RIGHT WING IGNORAMUSES.

WHERE'S YOUR GLOBAL WARMING *NOW* AL GORE?

HAW HAW HAW

AND: AS EGYPTIANS OVER-THROW MUBARAK, AMERI-CANS CHEER FOR DEMOCRACY!

IT'S SO *INSPIRING* WHEN ONE OF OUR CLIENT DICTATORS IS TOPPLED!

FEB. 7: VERY SERIOUS DEFICIT COMMISSION CO-CHAIR ALAN SIMPSON CALLS SOCIAL SECURITY--

"--A MILK COW WITH 300 MILLION *TEATS!*"

MAR. 7: ALAN SIMPSON COMPLAINS THAT YOUNG PEOPLE ARE "WALKING ON THEIR PANTS WITH THE CAP ON BACKWARDS LISTENING TO THE ENEMA MAN AND SNOOPY SNOOPY POOP DOGG!"

APRIL: G.O.P FIGHTS TO ELIMINATE GOV'T FUNDING FOR FAMILY PLANNING.

CONDOMS ARE JUST A SNEAKY WAY OF HAVING A *VERY* EARLY TERM ABORTION!

ALSO: DONALD TRUMP STAKES HIS SHORT-LIVED PRESIDENTIAL HOPES ON OBAMA'S BIRTH CERTIFICATE.

I THINK THERE ARE *SERIOUS QUESTIONS*--

AHEM.

APR. 2: COMPANY THAT OPERATED DEEPWATER HORIZON AWARDS EXECS SAFETY BONUSES.

IF YOU IGNORE THAT *ONE LITTLE ACCIDENT*--

--WE HAD A *GREAT* YEAR IN 2010!

MAY 1: BIN LADEN KILLED. OBAMA DECLARES "WE CAN DO WHATEVER WE SET OUR MIND TO."

AS LONG AS WHAT WE SET OUR MIND TO IS KILLING SOMEBODY.

FIXING THE ECONOMY, NOT SO MUCH.

MAY 26: SENATORS WYDEN & UDALL SEEM TO BE TRYING TO WARN US ABOUT SOMETHING.

IF YOU KNEW WHAT *WE* KNOW ABOUT THE PATRIOT ACT--

--YOU'D POOP YOUR *PANTS!**

*SLIGHT PARAPHRASE.

MAY 26: OBAMA NONE-THELESS SIGNS FOUR YEAR EXTENSION OF SAID ACT.

OH WELL! WE WEREN'T USING THOSE CIVIL LIBER-TIES *ANYWAY!*

JUNE 16: ANDREW BREITBART AQUIRES PICS OF ANTHONY WEINER'S PENIS; WORLD'S STUPIDEST SCANDAL ENSUES.

I CAN NEITHER CONFIRM NOR DENY THE IDENTITY OF THAT PENIS.

NEXT WEEK: MORE CRAZY!

TOM TOMORROW ©2011 ...www.thismodernworld.com...twitter.com/tomtomorrow

THIS MODERN WORLD

by TOM TOMORROW

2011

AN ADMITTEDLY INCOMPLETE AND UTTERLY SUBJECTIVE **YEAR IN REVIEW**

PART THE SECOND (YES, IT *IS* VERY WORDY)

MOST OF THE SUMMER: OBAMA REPEATEDLY TRIES TO STRIKE A "GRAND BARGAIN" WITH REPUBLICANS.

PLEASE, MAY I OFFER FURTHER CONCESSIONS?

NO.

AUG. 12: ALLEGEDLY SERIOUS PRESIDENTIAL CANDIDATE HERMAN CAIN TELLS CROWD--

"--A POET ONCE SAID 'LIFE CAN BE A CHALLENGE, LIFE CAN SEEM IMPOSSIBLE...'"

IT IS THE THEME SONG FROM A POKEMON MOVIE.

SEPT. 12: RON PAUL SAYS UNINSURED "TAKE (THEIR) OWN RISKS"; G.O.P. CROWD CHEERS AT THOUGHT OF HYPOTHETICAL PERSON DYING DUE TO LACK OF INSURANCE.

WHICH ACTUALLY HAPPENED TO ONE OF RON PAUL'S OWN STAFFERS IN 2008.

SEPT. 20: "DON'T ASK DON'T TELL" REPEALED; REPUBLIC FAILS TO COLLAPSE.

SEPT. 22: DEMONSTRATING THEIR UNCONDITIONAL RESPECT AND GRATITUDE FOR MILITARY SERVICE, G.O.P. CROWD BOOS SOLDIER FOR BEING GAY.

SEPT. 24: OCCUPY WALL STREET GAINS TRACTION WHEN VIDEO OF COP MACING PEACEFUL PROTESTERS GOES VIRAL.

NICE WORK, DUMBASS.

ALSO: THANKS TO THE OCCUPY MOVEMENT, PUNDITS BEGIN TO REALIZE THAT ORDINARY AMERICANS DON'T GIVE A RAT'S ASS ABOUT THE DEFICIT.

APPARENTLY THEY WANT "JOBS."

WHO KNEW?

SEPT. 30: U.S. GOV'T ASSASSINATES U.S. CITIZEN ACCUSED OF TERRORISM.

I GOTCHER DUE PROCESS RIGHT *HERE!*

A FEW WEEKS LATER: U.S. GOV'T KILLS HIS TEENAGE SON.

OCTOBER 29: FREAK SNOWSTORM ALONG EAST COAST MEANS...OH, YOU KNOW.

YARGLE BARGLE *BLARGH* AL GORE!

HAW HAW HAW

NOV. 1: HOUSE VOTES TO REAFFIRM "IN GOD WE TRUST" AS NATIONAL MOTTO.

JUST IN CASE ANYONE THOUGHT WE HAD STARTED WORSHIPPING *CTHULHU!*

NOV. 9: ALLEGEDLY SERIOUS CANDIDATE HERMAN CAIN DECLARES: "FOR EVERY ONE PERSON THAT COMES FORWARD WITH A FALSE ACCUSATION, THERE ARE PROBABLY *THOUSANDS* WHO WILL SAY NONE OF THAT SORT OF ACTIVITY EVER CAME FROM HERMAN CAIN!"

NOV. 21: "SUPER-COMMITTEE" FAILS TO ACHIEVE MAGICAL BIPARTISAN DEFICIT-REDUCING COMPROMISE.

NO ONE COULD HAVE FORESEEN *THIS!*

NOV. 30: MICHELE BACHMANN SAYS GAYS *DO* HAVE THE RIGHT TO MARRY.

"THEY CAN MARRY A MAN IF THEY'RE A WOMAN, OR THEY CAN MARRY A WOMAN IF THEY'RE A MAN."

SERIOUSLY, SHE SAID THAT.

DEC. 15: DEFENSE BILL CODIFIES INDEFINITE MILITARY DETENTION OF U.S. CITIZENS ON U.S. SOIL.

BUT THE *INNOCENT* HAVE NOTHING TO FEAR!

MONTH OF DECEMBER: INCREASINGLY DESPERATE G.O.P. CONTEMPLATES PRESIDENTIAL VIABILITY OF DISGRACED FORMER HOUSE SPEAKER WITH LONG HISTORY OF ADULTERY.

ON THE PLUS SIDE, HE'S *NOT MITT ROMNEY!*

ALL OF 2011: MORE LUNACY THAN WE COULD FIT IN AN ENTIRE *YEAR'S* WORTH OF CARTOONS--

--THOUGH OF COURSE WE *TRIED!*

HAPPY HOLIDAYS FROM TMW! SEE YOU NEXT YEAR!

www.thismodernworld.com...twitter.com/tomtomorrow

TOM TOMORROW ©2011

THIS MODERN WORLD

by TOM TOMORROW

Panel 1:

GREETINGS, EARTH-PENGUIN! MY STUDY OF YOUR NATION-STATE'S POLITICAL PROCESS CONTINUES-- AND I MUST CONFESS THAT I AM INCREASINGLY *CONFUSED*.

"EARTH-PENGUIN"..?

Panel 2:

CAN I POSSIBLY BE UNDERSTANDING THIS CORRECTLY--THAT THE FIRST STEP IN WINNOWING DOWN THE FIELD OF CANDIDATES CONSISTS OF A PECULIAR, UNDEMOCRATIC RITUAL IN A NOTABLY UNREPRESENTATIVE, SPARSELY-POPULATED RURAL STATE--

Panel 3:

--AND THAT THE APPARENT *WINNERS* OF THIS PROCESS WERE-- IN ASCENDING ORDER--A CANDIDATE WHO DESPISES THE VERY *IDEA* OF THE GOVERNMENT HE SEEKS TO LEAD...A CANDIDATE WHO SEEMS PRIMARILY MOTIVATED BY HIS DESIRE TO LEGISLATE THE SPECIFICS OF ALLOWABLE *MATING BEHAVIOR*...

Panel 4:

...AND THE PROBABLE EVENTUAL NOMINEE--AN INDIVIDUAL WITH *NO* ASCERTAINABLE CORE VALUES? *THESE* ARE THE MOST QUALIFIED CONTENDERS THE TRIBAL GROUPING COLLECTIVELY SELF-IDENTIFIED AS "REPUBLICANS" COULD *FIND*?

CERTAINLY I MUST BE MISSING SOMETHING.

NO, THAT PRETTY MUCH SUMS IT UP.

Panel 5:

Panel 6:

OKAY, THEN--NEXT QUESTION. EXPLAIN TO ME, PLEASE, THE PURPOSE OF THE INSTITUTION KNOWN AS THE "ELECTORAL COLLEGE."

SORRY. BETTER MINDS THAN MINE HAVE TRIED AND FAILED TO ANSWER *THAT*.

TOM TOMORROW ©2012....www.thismodernworld.com....twitter.com/tomtomorrow

THIS MODERN WORLD

by TOM TOMORROW

Panel 1: THE NOT-TOO-DISTANT-PAST: MITT ROMNEY HAS A LIFE-CHANGING *REVELATION!*

MY HISTORY OF PREDATORY CAPITALISM WAS *COMPLETELY AT ODDS* WITH MY RELIGIOUS FAITH!

THERE'S ONLY ONE THING FOR ME TO DO *NOW!*

I'LL DROP OUT OF PUBLIC LIFE-- AND SEEK *ATONEMENT!*

Panel 2: SHORTLY THEREAFTER...

--AND THE LAST ANYONE HEARD, HE WAS WORKING WITH *ORPHANS* IN *MUMBAI!*

WE'VE SPENT TOO MUCH TIME POSITIONING HIM FOR THE PRESIDENCY TO GIVE UP *NOW!*

CAN YOU *HELP* US, DR. VON PHILBERT?

OBVIOUSLY.

Panel 3: USING THE DNA FROM A STRAND OF MITT ROMNEY'S *HAIR*, THE BRILLIANT DOCTOR GETS TO WORK... AND *SOON...*

GENTLEMEN, I GIVE YOU THE *ROMDROID ONE!* HE'S A FUSION OF CLONING AND ROBOTICS, WHOSE BELIEF SYSTEM IS *COMPLETELY PROGRAMMABLE!*

HE'S THE *PERFECT* POLITICIAN!

Panel 4: AND JUST FOR THE SAKE OF EFFICIENCY--I WENT AHEAD AND CREATED THE *ROMDROID TWO!*

WE'LL CAMPAIGN *TWICE* AS HARD!

WHAT COULD POSSIBLY GO *WRONG?*

② ①

Panel 5: UNFORTUNATELY THE TWO ROMDROIDS ARE NEVER ABLE TO PROPERLY SYNC UP WITH ONE ANOTHER.

I REFORMED HEALTH CARE! | I'LL REPEAL OBAMACARE!

CLIMATE CHANGE IS MANMADE! | CLIMATE CHANGE IS A MYSTERY!

I'M PRO-CHOICE! | I'M PRO-LIFE!

Panel 6: AND CANDIDATE ROMNEY DEVELOPS A REPUTATION AS AN UNPRINCIPLED FLIP-FLOPPER.

IT'S BETTER THAN HAVING PEOPLE THINK HE'S A TWIN PAIR OF ROBOT-CLONES WITH A *PROGRAMMING GLITCH!*

EXCELLENT POINT!

Panel 7: BUT WAIT--WHAT'S *THIS?*

NO ONE WILL EVER BELIEVE THE *TRUTH*-- BUT I *MUST* DO SOMETHING!

TOM TOMORROW ©2012....www.thismodernworld.com...twitter.com/tomtomorrow

THIS MODERN WORLD

by TOM TOMORROW

THE ADVENTURES OF BEDBUG-MAN
AN ANTI-HERO FOR OUR TIMES

LATE ONE NIGHT IN THE OVAL OFFICE...

GAH! WHO THE HELL ARE **YOU**?

AND HOW DID YOU GET **IN** HERE?

I AM **BEDBUG-MAN**--THE SUPERHERO WITH THE PROPORTIONATE POWERS OF A **BEDBUG!**

I CAN HIDE ALMOST **ANYWHERE**-- AND I'M **REALLY** ANNOYING!

I FEEL ITCHY JUST **LOOKING** AT YOU.

I HAVE THAT EFFECT ON PEOPLE.

I'M HERE TO PESTER **YOU** ABOUT YOUR DECISION TO SIGN THE **NDAA**-- CODIFYING THE INDEFINITE DETENTION OF **AMERICAN CITIZENS!**

LOOK, I ISSUED A SIGNING STATEMENT-- PROMISING NEVER TO **ABUSE** THE AUTHORITY--

AND I'M SURE THAT WILL BE OF **GREAT** COMFORT TO WHOEVER ENDS UP ROTTING IN A JAIL CELL WHEN SOME **FUTURE** ADMINISTRATION INEVITABLY **DOES** ABUSE THE POWER YOU'VE SIGNED INTO LAW!

--BUT IN YOUR CASE MAYBE I'LL MAKE AN EXCEPTION.

WAIT, WHAT?

SEND IN SECURITY PLEASE.

BUT THEN--
I LOOKED AWAY FOR A **SECOND**-- AND HE WAS **GONE!**

NO ONE COULD DISAPPEAR **THAT** QUICKLY!

EXCEPT, PERHAPS, A HUMAN BEING WITH THE PROPORTIONATE POWERS OF A **BEDBUG!**

AND LATER...

OKAY, BUT SERIOUSLY--ABOUT THAT **SIGNING STATEMENT**--

GAH! YOU ARE **VERY** ANNOYING!

WHERE WILL HE TURN UP **NEXT**?!

THIS MODERN WORLD

by TOM TOMORROW

NEWT GINGRICH COULD NOT BE ANY MORE REPELLENT IF HE WERE **LITERALLY** EXPOSED AS AN OOZING, REPTILLIAN CREATURE BENT ON GLOBAL DOMINATION.

PATHETIC HUMANS! HOW CAN YOU EVEN **BEGIN** TO COMPREHEND **MY** SUPERIOR INTELLECT--WHEN **YOUR** PUNY BRAINS ARE LITTLE MORE THAN USELESS **APPENDAGES**?

THOUGH ADMITTEDLY VERY **TASTY!**

(HIS DISCARDED "HUMAN" MASK)

OF COURSE IF HE **WERE**, HE'D JUST BLAME THE **MEDIA**.

SPEAKER GINGRICH, MANY AMERICANS WERE STARTLED TO LEARN THAT YOU ARE ACTUALLY SOME SORT OF LIZARD-MAN WITH A TASTE FOR HUMAN **BRAINS**!

HOW DO YOU RE-SPOND?

I'M **SHOCKED** THAT THE LIBERAL MEDIA WOULD STOOP SO **LOW** WHEN THERE ARE SO MANY BRAINS TO BE **HARVESTED**--

--ER, I MEAN, SO MANY **ISSUES** TO BE **ADDRESSED!**

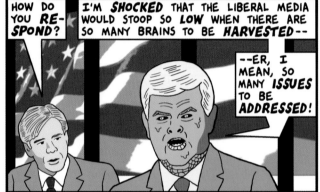

AND HIS DIEHARD SUPPORTERS WOULD OVERLOOK IT ALL IN ANY CASE.

WELL, I MEAN, SURE, HE'S A HIDEOUS, BRAIN-EATING **MONSTER**--

--BUT AT LEAST HE WON'T BE A "FOOD STAMP" PRESIDENT.

IF YOU KNOW WHAT WE MEAN.

AND WE THINK YOU DO.

AND THEN THERE'S **MITT ROMNEY**...WHO COULD NOT BE ANY LESS CONVINCING AS AN "ORDINARY GUY" IF HE **LITERALLY** WORE A TOP HAT AND MONOCLE...

WHAT HO! I BELIEVE I'LL POUR AN APPROPRIATE AMOUNT OF THIS GRANULATED SOAP PRODUCT INTO THE AUTOMATED CLOTHES-WASHING DEVICE!

JUST AS I DO **EVERY** WEEK!

PIP PIP! CHEERIO!

TOM TOMORROW ©2012....www.thismodernworld.com....twitter.com/tomtomorrow

THIS MODERN WORLD

by TOM TOMORROW

ONCE AGAIN, IT'S TIME TO JOURNEY INTO THE STRANGE, ALTERNATE REALITY OF THE

RIGHT-WINGO-VERSE

WHERE FACTS ARE A MATTER OF OPINION

IN THE RIGHTWINGOVERSE, THE FOUNDING FATHERS MOST CERTAINLY DID NOT OWN SLAVES.

IT'S A LIBERAL LIE PLANTED IN LIBERAL TEXTBOOKS BY LIBERAL HISTORIANS BECAUSE **LIBERALS HATE AMERICA!**

HAVE YOU NOT **HEARD** OF OCCAM'S RAZOR?

IN THE RIGHTWINGOVERSE, WALL STREET BANKERS BEAR NO RESPONSIBILITY FOR THE HOUSING CRASH.

THEY WERE **FORCED** TO MAKE BAD LOANS--UNDER THE **COMMUNITY REINVESTMENT ACT** OF 1977!

DEMOCRATS AND MINORITIES ARE ENTIRELY TO BLAME!

I HEARD ABOUT IT ON TALK RADIO--SO IT **MUST** BE TRUE!

IN THE RIGHTWINGOVERSE, EACH NEW SNOWFALL CONCLUSIVELY DISPROVES CLIMATE CHANGE--

THANKS FOR **NOTHING** AL GORE!

HAR HAR HAR!

--BUT RECORD HURRICANES, TORNADOES, AND FIFTY DEGREE WEATHER IN FEBRUARY MEAN NOTHING AT ALL.

:COUGH:

IN THE RIGHTWINGOVERSE, BARACK OBAMA PLAYS GOLF ALL THE TIME AND CAN'T SPEAK COHERENTLY WITHOUT A TELEPROMPTER.

UM--ARE YOU SURE YOU'RE NOT THINKING OF **GEORGE W. BUSH**?

SORRY, WHO?

NAME DOESN'T RING A BELL.

(IN THE RIGHTWINGOVERSE, NO ONE SEEMS TO REMEMBER WHO WAS PRESIDENT **BEFORE** OBAMA.)

IN THE RIGHTWINGOVERSE, **NEWT GINGRICH** IS AN ENTIRELY PLAUSIBLE PRESIDENTIAL CANDIDATE--

HE SUPPORTS TRADITIONAL MARRIAGE SO **FERVENTLY**--

--HE'S HAD **THREE WIVES!**

--BUT **NOBODY** HAS THE COMMON TOUCH LIKE **MITT ROMNEY.***

I SAY! IF YOU THINK **PETROL** PRICES ARE OUT OF CONTROL--

--TRY FUELING A **PRIVATE JET!**

TALLY **HO!**

*KIDDING! EVEN IN THE RIGHTWINGOVERSE, THEY'RE NOT **THAT** DELUSIONAL...

THIS MODERN WORLD

by TOM TOMORROW

Panel 1:

ON *PARALLEL EARTH*, IT'S MORE BAD NEWS FOR THE ROMNEY CAMPAIGN--AS BAIN CAPITAL'S INVOLVEMENT IN *HUMAN ORGAN HARVESTING* IS EXPOSED!

CORPORATIONS ARE *PEOPLE*, MY FRIEND! AND WE HAD PLENTY OF EXPERIENCE HARVESTING *THEIR* ASSETS!

THIS WAS JUST THE NEXT LOGICAL STEP.

Panel 2:

VICTIMS TELL THEIR *STORIES!*

I WOKE UP IN A BATHTUB FULL OF ICE WITH ONE OF MY *KIDNEYS* MISSING--

--AND A "ROMNEY FOR PRESIDENT" BUMPER STICKER PLASTERED OVER THE *INCISION!*

Panel 3:

BUT ROMNEY'S SUPPORTERS PUSH BACK *HARD!*

THESE ATTACKS ON BAIN'S INNOVATIVE ORGAN HARVESTING PROGRAM ARE NOTHING LESS THAN AN ASSAULT ON *CAPITALISM ITSELF!*

FOR THE LOVE OF GOD-- *LEAVE CAPITALISM ALOOOOONE!!*

Panel 4:

OF COURSE, THE GAFFE-PRONE CANDIDATE DOESN'T MAKE THINGS ANY *EASIER* FOR HIMSELF.

I'M NOT CONCERNED ABOUT POOR PEOPLE WHOSE ORGANS ARE HARVESTED AGAINST THEIR WILL!

WAIT, THAT CAME OUT WRONG.

I MEAN TO SAY, I *LIKE* HARVESTING ORGANS!

NO, WAIT--

Panel 5:

THE EXTENT TO WHICH IT COULD BE AN ISSUE IN THE GENERAL ELECTION REMAINS TO BE SEEN.

I'M *EXTREMELY* PRO-BUSINESS! I DON'T BEGRUDGE *ANYONE* THEIR SUCCESS!

I JUST THINK ORGAN HARVESTING MIGHT REPRESENT A *SLIGHT* OVERREACH.

GET A LOAD OF THE *COMMUNIST* HERE!

Panel 6:

IN THE *MEANTIME--*

--THIS JUST IN: BAIN CAPITAL WAS ALSO A MAJOR TRAFFICKER IN *SLAVE LABOR!*

MITT ROMNEY SMUGGLED SEDATED VICTIMS ACROSS THE BORDER IN A *DOG CARRIER* STRAPPED TO THE ROOF OF HIS *CAR!*

WOW! TALK ABOUT THE *INGENUITY* OF THE *FREE MARKET!*

Action McNews Network

THIS MODERN WORLD

by TOM TOMORROW

Panel 1:

HEY, YOUNG PEOPLE! IT'S TIME FOR ANOTHER EPISODE OF...

Sex Talk
with Rick Santorum

TODAY'S FRANK TOPIC: THE *EVIL* OF *CONTRACEPTION!*

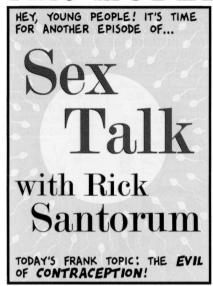

Panel 2:

YOU BOYS AND GIRLS WILL SOON BEGIN TO EXPERIENCE STRANGE NEW FEELINGS YOU MAY NOT ENTIRELY *UNDERSTAND*...AND THEN, WHEN YOU ARE OLD ENOUGH, YOU WILL GET MARRIED AND HAVE *PROCREATIVE SEX!*

THIS IS ENTIRELY NATURAL.

Panel 3:

WHAT'S *NOT* NATURAL IS TO INTERFERE WITH GOD'S DIVINE PLAN THROUGH THE USE OF SECULAR *BIRTH CONTROL* METHODS!

IF GOD *WANTED* YOU TO USE BIRTH CONTROL, HE'D WRITE YOU A PRESCRIPTION *HIMSELF!*

Panel 4:

WHICH IS NOT TO SAY SEX CAN'T BE *PLEASURABLE!* WHY, THE AVERAGE WOMAN OF CHILDBEARING AGE SHOULD BE ABLE TO ENJOY PROCREATIVE SEX ANYWHERE FROM *FIVE* TO *TEN TIMES* OVER THE COURSE OF HER LIFETIME!

Panel 5:

BUT--LISTEN CAREFULLY, BOYS AND GIRLS--THE IMPORTANT THING TO REMEMBER IS THAT PROCREATIVE SEX IS A DEEPLY *PERSONAL* AND PROFOUNDLY *INTIMATE* MATTER BETWEEN A HUSBAND AND WIFE--

Panel 6:

--*AND* THE UNITED STATES CONGRESS AND THE CELIBATE HIERARCHY OF THE CATHOLIC CHURCH.

AND ALSO REPUBLICAN PRESIDENTIAL CANDIDATES.

EXCEPT GINGRICH.

SERIOUSLY, DON'T LISTEN TO *THAT* GUY.

NEXT TIME: MASTURBATION IS *MURDER!*

ALSO: DON'T GOOGLE ME, PLEASE.

TOM TOMORROW © 2012...www.thismodernworld.com...twitter.com/tomtomorrow

THIS MODERN WORLD

by TOM TOMORROW

A NEW CULTURE-WAR CONTROVERSY **EXPLODES!**

THE PURSUIT OF THE **ORGASM** LEADS WOMEN TO HAVE **SEX**-- WHICH LEADS TO **ABORTIONS!**

AND THAT'S WHY THE **FEMALE ORGASM** IS A VIOLATION OF OUR **RELIGIOUS LIBERTY!**

CONSERVATIVE PUNDITS WEIGH IN**!**

THERE'S NOTHING IN THE CONSTITUTION THAT **GUARANTEES** THE RIGHT TO A **FEMALE ORGASM!**

IF SUCH A THING EVEN **EXISTS!**

I'VE CERTAINLY NEVER SEEN ONE**!**

WORRISOME HYPOTHETICAL SCENARIOS **PROLIFERATE!**

FOR INSTANCE--IF A FEMALE GOVERNMENT EMPLOYEE SPENDS PART OF HER PAY ON A **VIBRATOR**--

--AREN'T **WE** BEING FORCED TO SUBSIDIZE HER TAXPAYER-FUNDED **ORGASMS**?

I DEMAND AN EXEMPTION OF CONSCIENCE!

SENSIBLE MODERATES LOOK FOR COMMON GROUND.

CAN'T WE ALL AGREE THAT WOMEN SHOULD BE ALLOWED TO HAVE THE **OCCASIONAL** ORGASM, IN THE CONTEXT OF A SOCIETALLY-SANCTIONED MONOGAMOUS HETEROSEXUAL RELATIONSHIP--

--AS LONG AS IT DOESN'T **TAKE** TOO LONG?

BUT STATE LEGISLATORS IN VIRGINIA HAVE SOME IDEAS OF THEIR **OWN.**

WE BELIEVE WOMEN SUSPECTED OF ORGASMS SHOULD BE FORCED TO SUBMIT TO AN **INVASIVE GYNECOLOGICAL EXAM!**

NO REASON! WE JUST WANT TO SHOW THEM WHO'S **BOSS!**

TOO BAD OUR **GOVERNOR** CAVED TO THE **ORGASM LOBBY!**

OF COURSE, IT'S IMPORTANT TO MAKE CERTAIN **DISTINCTIONS** IN A DEBATE LIKE THIS.

OBVIOUSLY THE **MALE** ORGASM IS BIOLOGICALLY NECESSARY FOR REPRODUCTION**!**

INDEED! IF GOD HAD INTENDED **WOMEN** TO HAVE ORGASMS--

--HE WOULD HAVE GIVEN THEM **PENISES!**

TOM TOMORROW ©2012....www.thismodernworld.com....twitter.com/tomtomorrow

THIS MODERN WORLD

by TOM TOMORROW

ONCE AGAIN, IT'S TIME TO PEER THROUGH THE **PARALLELOSCOPE**-- AND SEE HOW THE DOPPELGANGER PRIMARY SEASON ON **PARALLEL EARTH** IS UNFOLDING...

THERE, AS HERE, MITT ROMNEY IS HAVING TROUBLE CONNECTING WITH VOTERS...

LIKE MANY TYPICAL HUMANS, I **ENJOY** PERSONAL VEHICULAR TRANSIT! AS WELL AS **TREES**, AS LONG AS THEY ARE APPROPRIATELY SIZED!

IN FACT, I AM **SEVERELY** HUMAN!

WHY ARE YOU ALL MAKING THE INVOLUNTARY NOISE WHICH INDICATES **AMUSEMENT**?

...WHILE RICK SANTORUM REMAINS UNAPOLOGETICALLY **MEDIEVAL**.

THE SECULARISTS **NEVER** EXPECTED **ME** TO MAKE IT THIS FAR! BUT THEN AGAIN--

--NOBODY EXPECTS THE **PENNSYLVANIA INQUISITION**!!

NEWT GINGRICH, OF COURSE, IS REPELLENT IN **ANY** UNIVERSE.

YOU AFGHANS ARE GOING TO HAVE TO LEARN TO LIVE YOUR **OWN** MISERABLE LIVES!

BECAUSE CLEARLY YOU HAVEN'T LEARNED A **THING** FROM OUR **DEMOCRACY DRONES** AND **FREEDOM BOMBS**!

LOSERS.

OVERALL, THE REPUBLICAN PARTY IS JUST AS BONKERS.

YOU KNOW WHAT I **REALLY** HATE? THE **MUPPETS**! ALSO, CONTRACEPTION, BREAST CANCER SCREENING, AND THE **GIRL SCOUTS**!

AND THAT'S JUST **THIS** MONTH!

BUT THERE'S ONE IMPORTANT DIFFERENCE: ON **PARALLEL** EARTH, THE G.O.P. BASE HAS THE CHAMPION FOR WHICH IT **YEARNS**.

VOTE **UGG**! UGG MIGHTY **WARRIOR**! UGG SMASH **ENEMIES**!

WOMEN **OBEY** UGG AND MAKE **BABIES**--LIKE FIRE GOD **INTEND**!

TALK ABOUT **TRADITIONAL VALUES**!

HE'S SURE GOT **MY** VOTE!

TOM TOMORROW © 2012....www.thismodernworld.com....twitter.com/tomtomorrow

by TOM TOMORROW

SO ERIC HOLDER SAYS THE U.S. GOVERNMENT CAN ASSASSINATE ANYONE WHO'S BEEN SECRETLY DECLARED GUILTY OF TERRORISM.

ASSASSINATION IS ILLEGAL. I BELIEVE YOU ARE REFERRING TO "TARGETED KILLING."

WHATEVER YOU WANT TO CALL IT--THE EXECUTIVE BRANCH HAS EFFECTIVELY GRANTED ITSELF THE AUTHORITY OF UNILATERAL *EXE-CUTION*.

I TRUST THE PRESIDENT TO USE THIS POWER FOR GOOD AND NOT EVIL.

OKAY--BUT WHAT ABOUT DOWN THE ROAD, WHEN THERE'S A PRESIDENT YOU *DON'T* TRUST--

--WHO USES THIS PRECEDENT TO JUSTIFY SOMETHING EVEN *YOU* FIND ABHORRENT?

WHEN THAT HAPPENS, I PROMISE TO BE *VERY, VERY* OUTRAGED.

IF ANYONE NEEDS ME, I'LL BE IN THE OTHER ROOM BANGING MY HEAD AGAINST THE WALL.

OKEY DOKEY!

TOM TOMORROW © 2012....www.thismodernworld.com....twitter.com/tomtomorrow

THIS MODERN WORLD

by TOM TOMORROW

OUR TOP STORY TONIGHT-- A GIANT UNSTOPPABLE ASTEROID IS PLUMMETING TOWARD OUR PLANET!

AS WE FACE THE CERTAIN EXTINCTION OF ALL LIFE ON EARTH, THE QUESTION ON EVERYONE'S MIND IS--

Action McNews Network

--HOW WILL THIS AFFECT THE 2012 *PRESIDENTIAL RACE*?

I'M VERY CONCERNED ABOUT THE DESTRUCTION OF THIS PLANET! I KNOW MANY OF ITS OWNERS!

REPENT, SINNERS! AND VOTE FOR *ME*!

I'M IN THIS 'TIL THE *END*!

LITERALLY.

WE TURN NOW FOR EXPERT ANALYSIS FROM OUR RESIDENT EXPERT GUYS!

NO QUESTION ABOUT IT--THIS IS GOING TO HURT OBAMA IN THE POLLS!

Action McNews Network

IT'S LIKE A ONE-TWO PUNCH FOR THE AVERAGE AMERICAN WORKER--FIRST, RISING *GAS* PRICES--

--AND *NOW*, THE OBLITERATION OF ALL THEY KNOW AND LOVE!

SO DOES THE PROSPECT OF IMPENDING PLANETARY DOOM MEAN THAT THE G.O.P. WILL *FINALLY* RALLY AROUND *ROMNEY*?

OH, IT WOULD TAKE MORE THAN *THAT*.

THEY *REALLY* DON'T LIKE THAT GUY.

BUT THE CERTAINTY OF IMMINENT ANNIHILATION *COULD* SUPPRESS THE YOUTH VOTE IN THE *GENERAL* ELECTION--IN WHICH CASE THE DESTRUCTION OF THE PLANET WOULD BE *GOOD NEWS* FOR *REPUBLICANS*!

AT LEAST UNTIL, YOU KNOW, THE DESTRUCTION OF THE PLANET.

ALL RIGHT, GENTLMEN-- THANK YOU FOR YOUR *INSIGHT*!

COMING UP NEXT: WHAT DOES THE END OF THE WORLD MEAN FOR *YOUR* STOCK PORTFOLIO?

ALSO--HOW ARE YOUR FAVORITE *CELEBRITIES* COPING WITH THE STRESS?

FIRST THESE *MESSAGES*!

Action McNews Network

TOM TOMORROW © 2012....www.thismodernworld.com....twitter.com/tomtomorrow

THIS MODERN WORLD

by TOM TOMORROW

Panel 1: "STAND YOUR GROUND" LAWS ARE BASICALLY A LICENSE TO *KILL*.

Panel 2: IT'S RACIST GUN-NUTTERY, CODIFIED INTO *LAW*.

HEY! WATCH YOUR LANGUAGE, YOU ANTI-GUNNITE.

Panel 3: THE SHOOTER IN FLORIDA WAS SIMPLY EXERCISING HIS RIGHT OF SELF-DEFENSE AS A GUN-OWNING AMERICAN.

WHO LIVES IN FLORIDA.

BUT THE KID WASN'T *DOING* ANYTHING!

Panel 4: HE LOOKED *SUSPICIOUS!* AND IF YOU ASK *ME*, THE BURDEN OF PROOF IS *ALWAYS* ON THE SUSPICIOUS-LOOKING PERSON!

ESPECIALLY IF HE'S--YOU KNOW-- WEARING A *HOODIE!*

Panel 6: THERE'S REALLY JUST NEVER GOING TO BE A "TEACHABLE MOMENT" WITH YOU, IS THERE?

YOU'LL PRY *MY* BELIEF SYSTEM FROM MY COLD, DEAD BRAIN.

SO WHAT IF A BLACK GUY WITH A GUN FINDS *YOU* SUSPICIOUS?

HAW! WHAT AN IMAGINATION YOU HAVE!

TOM TOMORROW ©2012...www.thismodernworld.com...twitter.com/tomtomorrow

84

THIS MODERN WORLD

by TOM TOMORROW

HEALTH CARE REFORM: A BRIEF GLOSSARY OF TERMS

1) SINGLE PAYER: RATIONAL HEALTH CARE SYSTEM, DEEMED POLITICALLY UNPALATABLE TO LOW-INFORMATION VOTERS.

UNIVERSAL HEALTH CARE IS THE FIRST STEP ON THE PATH TO **COMMUNIST TYRANNY!**

LIKE UP THERE IN **CANADA!**

2) INSURANCE INDUSTRY PROFIT: PRIMARY PURPOSE OF AMERICAN HEALTH SYSTEM AS CURRENTLY STRUCTURED.

HERE'S HOW IT WORKS: YOU PAY US **PREMIUMS**--

--AND **WE** LOOK FOR REASONS TO DENY YOU **COVERAGE.**

3) PUBLIC OPTION: WATERED-DOWN VERSION OF SINGLE PAYER; WOULD HAVE PROVIDED ALTERNATIVE TO PRIVATE INSURERS. DEEMED UNPALATABLE TO INSURANCE INDUSTRY.

COMPETITION IS WELL AND GOOD, BUT LET'S NOT GET CARRIED **AWAY.**

4) INDIVIDUAL MANDATE: MARKET-DRIVEN PLAN FIRST PROPOSED BY CONSERVATIVE HERITAGE FOUNDATION AND FIRST IMLEMENTED BY MITT ROMNEY.

IT WILL BE A **TRIUMPH** OF BIPARTISANSHIP! HOW CAN MY REPUBLICAN FRIENDS **OBJECT**?

IT'S **THEIR PLAN!**

5) SOCIALISM: TERM USED BY G.O.P. TO DESCRIBE HERITAGE PLAN AFTER ADOPTION BY OBAMA.

"INDIVIDUAL MANDATE"? WHAT IS THAT, FRENCH FOR "**GOVERNMENT DEATH PANELS**"?

I BLAME **SAUL ALINSKY!**

ER--YES! QUITE RIGHT! I TOO AM OUTRAGED!

6) SUPREME COURT: JUDICIAL BODY WITH POWER TO OVERTURN OBAMACARE, THANKS TO ADOPTION OF INDIVIDUAL MANDATE.

ISN'T THIS EXACTLY LIKE FORCING PEOPLE TO EAT **BROCCOLI**?

I **HATE** BROCCOLI!

7) TRANSVAGINAL PROBES: THE ONLY HEALTH CARE MANDATE CONSERVATIVES CURRENTLY SUPPORT.

GOVERNMENT SHOULD KEEP ITS INVASIVE LAWS OFF OUR **BODIES!**

UNLESS WE ARE WOMEN SEEKING ABORTIONS.

WHICH WE ARE NOT.

TOM TOMORROW © 2012....www.thismodernworld.com....twitter.com/tomtomorrow

THIS MODERN WORLD

by TOM TOMORROW

GOOFBALL AND GALAHAD

GOOFBALL THINKS WE SHOULD ACKNOWLEDGE THE REALITY OF HUMAN MORTALITY.

WE ALL NEED HEALTH CARE SOONER OR LATER!

GALAHAD THINKS ILLNESS AND INJURY ARE MATTERS OF PERSONAL DISCRETION!

AMERICANS HAVE THE **FREEDOM** TO BE UNINSURED!

AND ANYWAY, YOU CAN **ALWAYS** GO TO THE EMERGENCY ROOM!

GOOFBALL BELIEVES IN THE SCIENCE OF GLOBAL CLIMATE CHANGE.

IF AVERAGE TEMPERATURES RISE SIX DEGREES BY THE END OF THE CENTURY, LARGE PARTS OF THE PLANET BECOME UNINHABITABLE!

GALAHAD BELIEVES WHAT HE HEARS ON TALK RADIO!

CLIMATE SCIENTISTS ARE **BIASED!** UNLIKE THE UTTERLY IMPARTIAL **ENERGY INDUSTRY!**

GOOFBALL WONDERS WHAT HAPPENS WHEN THE OIL RUNS OUT.

DOESN'T IT MAKE SENSE TO START TRANSITIONING TO NEW TECHNOLOGIES **NOW?**

GALAHAD REFUSES TO ENTERTAIN THE POSSIBILITY!

THE ONLY ENERGY POLICY **WE** NEED IS TO **DRILL BABY DRILL**--LIKE GOD **INTENDED!**

GOOFBALL UNDERSTANDS THAT PEOPLE HAVE SEX WHEN THEY GET OLDER.

SO THEY SHOULD BE REALISTIC ABOUT CONTRACEPTION. I MEAN, **I** KNOW THAT MUCH.

GALAHAD'S THOUGHTS ON THE TOPIC ARE A LITTLE MORE **CONFUSED.**

THE DIRTY LIBERAL SLUTS WANT THE GOVERNMENT TO BUY THEM BIRTH CONTROL FOR ALL THE DIRTY **SEX** THEY HAVE!

IT IS AN **OUTRAGE!**

AND MAKES ME FEEL FUNNY INSIDE.

TOM TOMORROW © 2012...www.thismodernworld.com...twitter.com/tomtomorrow

THIS MODERN WORLD

by TOM TOMORROW

THE ONGOING ADVENTURES OF SPARKMAN AND THE BLINKSTER

A CHANCE ENCOUNTER NEAR AN *OCCUPY* DEMONSTRATION...

HA HA! LOOK AT THE IDIOT PROTESTERS GETTING ARRESTED!

ENJOY YOUR *STRIP SEARCHES*, MORONS!

AHEM.

THANKS TO THE SUPREME COURT-- *AND* THE OBAMA D.O.J.--IT'S TRUE THAT ANYONE ARRESTED FOR ANY MINOR INFRACTION NOW FACES A HUMILIATING *BODY CAVITY SEARCH.*

BUT AM I TO INFER THAT YOU FIND THIS LATEST ASSAULT ON CIVIL LIBERTIES *AMUSING*?

TOTALLY! THOSE OCCUPIERS ARE ABOUT TO GET *OCCUPIED!*

IF YOU KNOW WHAT I *MEAN!* HEH HEH!

SIGH...BLINKSTER, I'M AFRAID THIS IS A JOB FOR THE--THE--

YOU MEAN THE--

YES--

--THE HEAVY-HANDED RAY OF IRONIC JUSTICE!

BZZRRAAAP

WHAT THE--?

WAIT FOR IT...

HOLD IT RIGHT THERE! YOU'RE UNDER ARREST--FOR *UNLAWFUL ASSEMBLY!*

BUT--BUT *I'M* NOT A PROTESTER!

YOU CAN TELL IT TO THE *JUDGE*, PAL-- AFTER YOUR *RECTAL EXAM!*

ULP!

WOW! THAT WAS IRONIC--*AND* HEAVY-HANDED!

WITH GREAT POWER COMES GREAT RESPONSIBILITY, OLD CHUM.

NEXT: WHAT DO *I* CARE IF THEY LOOK IN MY RECTUM? *I'VE* GOT NOTHING TO HIDE!

UH OH.

TOM TOMORROW © 2012...www.thismodernworld.com...twitter.com/tomtomorrow

THIS MODERN WORLD

by TOM TOMORROW

MITT ROMNEY MAN OF THE PEOPLE

WE ARE NOT SO VERY DIFFERENT, YOU AND I--

--EXCEPT THAT **I'M** RICH BEYOND DREAMS OF **AVARICE!!**

BOY! THERE WAS THIS ONE TIME, I GOT STUCK IN AN ELEVATOR--

--IN ONE OF MY WIFE'S MANY **CADILLACS!!**

LET ME REGALE YOU WITH AN AMUSING ANECDOTE--

--ABOUT **PEOPLE GETTING FIRED!**

THAT ONE NEVER GETS OLD.

MY TURN!

WHEN MITT AND I WERE YOUNG, WE WERE SO POOR--

--WE HAD TO **LIVE OFF OUR INVESTMENT INCOME!!**

WE WERE PRACTICALLY **HOBOS!**

HEH HEH   HEH

OH FOR GOODNESS SAKES--CAN'T WE JUST **BUY** THE WHITE HOUSE?

I DON'T THINK YOU'RE SUPPOSED TO SAY THAT OUT LOUD, DEAR.

MEANWHILE

YES, THAT'S RIGHT--I WAS BITTEN ...BY A **PENGUIN!**

www.thismodernworld.com...www.twitter.com/tomtomorrow

TOM TOMORROW ©2012

THIS MODERN WORLD

by TOM TOMORROW

THE ADVENTURES OF CONSERVATIVE JONES CITIZEN JOURNALIST

MOONBAT! COME IN! YOU'RE JUST IN TIME!

HEY DUDE, I--OH DEAR GOD, DO I EVEN WANT TO *ASK* WHAT YOU'RE DOING THIS TIME?

I'M PREPARING FOR AN UNDER-COVER CITIZEN JOURNALIST INVESTI-GATION--OF THE LOCAL *PLANNED PARENTHOOD* OFFICE!

I'VE GOT A VIDEO CAMERA HIDDEN IN MY *BRASSIERE!*

OF COURSE YOU DO.

I PLAN TO RECORD THEM ADMITTING THEY'LL PERFORM SEX-SELECTIVE ABORTIONS FOR PEOPLE WHO JUST DON'T WANT BABY *GIRLS!* THAT SHOULD STIR UP SOME TROUBLE!

BUT--YOU DON'T SERIOUSLY *BELIEVE*--

OF COURSE NOT. DO I *LOOK* LIKE A MORON?

BUT THERE ARE PLENTY OF PEOPLE OUT THERE WHO *WILL* BELIEVE IT--ESPECIALLY AFTER MY VIDEO GOES *VIRAL!*

SEE, ALL I *REALLY* NEED IS TO RECORD THEM SAYING "YES" OR "NO"--I CAN DUB THE *QUESTIONS* IN *LATER!*

WELL, I DON'T SEE ANYTHING THAT COULD POSSIBLY GO WRONG WITH *THIS* PLAN.

DO YOU THINK MY BOOBS ARE BIG ENOUGH?

I'M GOING TO LEAVE NOW.

NEXT TIME WANT TO SEE THE DIS-GUISE FOR MY UPCOMING *MINORITY VOTE FRAUD* INVESTIGATION?

NO. NO, I GENUINELY DO NOT.

...www.thismodernworld.com....twitter.com/tomtomorrow

TOM TOMORROW © 2012....

THIS MODERN WORLD

by TOM TOMORROW

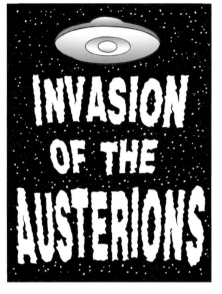

INVASION OF THE AUSTERIONS

THEY ARRIVE FROM A DISTANT GALAXY, BEARING A MESSAGE OF ECONOMIC SALVATION.

PEOPLE OF EARTH--WE ARE THE **AUSTERIONS!**

REDUCE YOUR **DEFICITS** TO SPUR INVESTOR **CONFIDENCE!**

THE AUSTER-IONS HAVE **SPOKEN.**

THE ALIEN DOCTRINE FINDS A RECEPTIVE AUDIENCE ON EARTH!

THE AUSTERIONS SAY THE NATIONS OF THE WORLD MUST **UNITE** IN BALANCING THEIR BUDGETS ON THE BACKS OF THE POOR, MR. NORQUIST!

WHO ARE **WE** TO ARGUE WITH THEIR ADVANCED ECONOMIC KNOWLEDGE, MR. RYAN?

OF COURSE THERE ARE **SOME** POCKETS OF RESISTANCE.

FRENCH AND GREEK VOTERS UNDER-STAND--THIS IS **MADNESS!** YOU CAN'T SLASH SPENDING IN THE MIDDLE OF A RECESSION WITHOUT EXACERBATING THE UNDERLYING--

URRK!

FOOLISH HUMAN.

BZRAAAP!

EVENTUALLY...

HELP US, AUSTERIONS! THE GLOBAL ECONOMY HAS **FLATLINED!** OUR CITIES ARE IN **CHAOS!**

EXCELLENT! YOUR JOB CREATORS SHOULD BE FEELING "CONFIDENT" ANY **DAY** NOW!

SO SAYETH THE **AUSTERIONS!**

BUT **THEN--**

HEH! EARTH WILL SOON BE OURS FOR THE **TAKING!**

REMEMBER WHEN WE NEEDED A FLEET OF **BATTLE CRUISERS** TO CONQUER A PLANET LIKE THIS?

IT'S **SO** MUCH EASIER TO SIT BACK--AND WATCH THEM DESTROY **THEMSELVES!**

TOM TOMORROW © 2012....www.thismodernworld.com....twitter.com/tomtomorrow

THIS MODERN WORLD

by TOM TOMORROW

Drone Industry Planning Public Relations Campaign

HEY KIDS! IT'S ME, *DRONEY*--

--THE *FRIENDLY* SURVEILLANCE DRONE!

DRONES HAVE BEEN GETTING SOME BAD PRESS LATELY! I TELL YA-- YOU ACCIDENTALLY WIPE OUT A FEW WEDDING PARTIES AND *SOME* PEOPLE WON'T SHUT *UP* ABOUT IT!

BUT YOU KIDS DON'T HAVE TO WORRY ABOUT THAT! *DOMESTIC* DRONES WON'T EVEN *HAVE* ANY WEAPONS!

EXCEPT MAY- BE IN SOME CASES.

LIKE, IF WE'RE AFTER A *REALLY* BAD GUY.

I'D STAY AWAY FROM WEDDING PARTIES JUST IN CASE.

AND SPEAKING OF SAFETY--LET ME ASSURE YOU THAT DRONES *ALMOST NEVER* LOSE CONTACT WITH THEIR CONTROLLERS AND FLY WILDLY OUT OF CONTROL BEFORE CRASHING INTO THE GROUND SOMEWHERE.

YOU SHOULD BE RELATIVE- LY SAFE.

WE'RE REASONABLY SURE OF IT!

NOW, I KNOW THE ACLU AND OTHER CHICKEN LITTLES HAVE RAISED CON- CERNS ABOUT *PRIVACY*. AND YOU KNOW WHAT I SAY ABOUT *THAT*?

UH--NO, WHAT?

I SAY IF YOU'RE NOT DOING ANYTHING *WRONG*--

--YOU DON'T HAVE ANYTHING TO *HIDE*--FROM *DRONEY*!

SAY--YOU KIDS *AREN'T* DOING ANYTHING WRONG, ARE YOU?

ER-- UH-- *NO*!

GREAT! WELL, I'VE GOT TO RUN, BUT I'LL BE *SEEING* YOU!

FROM ABOUT 6,000 FEET.

THE ROBOT DEATH PLANE SCARES ME.

I HEARD THAT.

TOM TOMORROW © 2012....www.thismodernworld.com...twitter.com/tomtomorrow

THIS MODERN WORLD

by TOM TOMORROW

HEY KIDS! YOU ALREADY KNOW HOW A **BILL** BECOMES A **LAW**! NOW LET'S TAKE A LOOK AT...

How a Secret Memo Justifies a Kill List!

FIRST, THE OFFICE OF LEGAL COUNSEL DRAFTS **ME**--A MEMO PROVIDING A LEGAL RATIONALE FOR SOMETHING THE PRESIDENT WANTS--LIKE AN EXTRAJUDICIAL PROGRAM OF **TARGETED ASSASSINATION**!

SO CAN I **READ** YOU?

OF **COURSE** NOT! I'M **SECRET**!

NEXT, THEY SEND ME OVER TO THE WHITE HOUSE--AND, WELL, THAT'S PRETTY MUCH **IT**!

THE PRESIDENT USES THE AUTHORITY PROVIDED BY **ME** TO CREATE MY COUSIN HERE--THE **KILL LIST**!

LOOK OUT, PROBABLE BAD GUYS! **MY** JUSTICE IS SWIFT--AND **UNILATERAL**!

BUT--WHAT ABOUT **DUE PROCESS**?

EXCELLENT QUESTION! THIS **IS** A GOVERNMENT OF LAWS, NOT MEN! AND WE BELIEVE THE REQUIREMENTS OF DUE PROCESS--WHEN APPLICABLE--ARE SATISFIED THROUGH **INTERNAL DELIBERATIONS** WITHIN THE EXECUTIVE BRANCH!

THOSE **OTHER** BRANCHES OF GOVERNMENT WOULD JUST BE IN THE **WAY**!

OKAY--BUT WHAT IF YOU KILL AN **INNOCENT PERSON**?

NOT TO WORRY! WE'RE **VERY** CAREFUL TO AVOID CIVILIAN CASUALTIES--

--BY LABELING **ANY** MILITARY-AGE MALE IN THE STRIKE ZONE A **COMBATANT**!

PROBLEM SOLVED!

AND **THAT**, MY BOY, IS HOW A **SECRET MEMO** IS USED TO JUSTIFY AN EXECUTIVE **KILL LIST**!

EXCUSE ME-- WHAT ABOUT **CHECKS** AND **BALANCES**?

OH GOD--NOT **YOU** AGAIN! CAN'T YOU TAKE A **HINT**, OLD TIMER?

SOME PIECES OF PAPER DON'T KNOW WHEN TO **QUIT**!

TOM TOMORROW © 2012....www.thismodernworld.com....twitter.com/tomtomorrow

93

THIS MODERN WORLD

by TOM TOMORROW

INVISIBLE-HAND-OF-THE FREE-MARKET MAN

I.H.O.T.F.M.-MAN--IN HIS SECRET IDENTITY AS MILD-MANNERED CONSULTANT **CLARK HANDY**--IS MEETING WITH MITT ROMNEY--

--SO WHEN **BAIN** COMES UP, YOU MUST ACCUSE **OBAMA** OF BEING THE **REAL** VULTURE CAPITALIST!

REPEAT AFTER ME: "I'M RUBBER, YOU'RE GLUE--"

--WHEN SUDDENLY--

MY **FREE MARKET SENSE**-- TINGLING LIKE **CRAZY**!

SORRY SIR--GOTTA RUN! I JUST REMEMBERED-- UM--A **FINANCIAL TRANSACTION** I HAVE TO CONDUCT!

THERE'S SOMETHING **FAMILIAR** ABOUT THAT FELLOW--BUT I CAN'T QUITE PUT MY **FINGER** ON IT...

MEANWHILE AT **FACEBOOK H.Q.**-- IT'S THE DREADED **REGULATOR**!

THERE ARE **SERIOUS QUESTIONS** ABOUT YOUR I.P.O., MR. ZUCKERBERG! INSTITUTIONAL INVESTORS WERE QUIETLY WARNED OF DECLINING REVENUES-- BUT **SMALL** INVESTORS WERE LEFT IN THE **DARK**!

AND YOUR POINT **IS**--?

BUT **THEN**--

PAY NO ATTENTION TO THIS SAD LITTLE MAN, SON! THERE'S ONLY **ONE RELEVANT QUESTION** TO ASK ABOUT YOUR I.P.O.--ARE YOU, PERSONALLY, NOW EVEN **MORE** INCOMPREHENSIBLY WEALTHY THAN YOU WERE BEFORE?

WELL, DUH.

THEN THE SYSTEM **WORKED**!

YOU CAN HIRE A BATTALION OF ATTORNEYS TO KEEP **HIM** BUSY.

UH, YEAH. THANKS FOR THE INPUT, CAPTAIN OBVIOUS.

SAY, ARE **YOU** ON FACEBOOK? I **PROMISE** NOT TO REVEAL YOUR SECRET IDENTITY!

AT LEAST, UNTIL WE REVISE OUR PRIVACY POLICY AGAIN.

LATER, DUDES.

OKAY! CAPITALISM TRIUMPHS AGAIN. I THINK.

KIDS TODAY. WHAT ARE YOU GONNA DO.

MEANWHILE BACK AT THE ROMNEY CAMPAIGN...

YOU KNOW, I'VE NEVER SEEN CLARK AND I.H.O.T.F.M.-MAN IN THE SAME **ROOM**! YOU DON'T **SUPPOSE**--?

DON'T BE ABSURD! **CLARK** WEARS GLASSES!

TOM TOMORROW © 2012....www.thismodernworld.com....twitter.com/tomtomorrow

THIS MODERN WORLD

by TOM TOMORROW

HEALTH CARE REFORM GLOSSARY UPDATED

1) HERITAGE FOUNDATION: CONSERVATIVE THINK TANK WHICH PROPOSED MARKET-BASED HEALTH CARE REFORM IN 1989.

WE CALL IT THE "*INDIVIDUAL MANDATE*"!

IT'S AN *INNOCULATION*--AGAINST *SOCIALIZED MEDICINE*!

2) ROMNEYCARE: VERSION OF HERITAGE PLAN INSTITUTED IN MASSACHUSETTS BY MITT ROMNEY, WHO NOW SEEMS TO HAVE NO MEMORY OF THE EVENT.

I DID *WHAT?*

SURELY YOU ARE *MISTAKEN!*

I LAUGH AT YOUR ERROR!

AH HA HA HA HA HA!

3) OBAMACARE: VERSION OF ROMNEYCARE EMBRACED BY BARACK OBAMA IN 2009.

A MARKET-BASED PLAN WHICH PRESERVES THE PRIMACY OF PRIVATE INSURERS? HOW COULD ANY REPUBLICAN POSSIBLY *OBJECT?*

4) IMAGINARY OBAMACARE: SOURCE OF MASS HYSTERIA AMONG CONSERVATIVES FOR THE PAST THREE YEARS.

HE WANTS TO KILL US *ALL* WITH HIS BIG-GOVERNMENT *DEATH PANELS!*

IT'S STRAIGHT OUT OF THE *COMMUNIST MANIFESTO!*

YARGLE BARGLE BLARGH!

5) CHIEF JUSTICE ROBERTS: SURPRISE SWING VOTE UPHOLDING HEALTH CARE REFORM, TO DISMAY OF MANY.

THAT TURNCOAT MAKES ME SICK TO MY *STOMACH!*

WELL, AT LEAST YOU'LL HAVE HEALTH CARE FOR THAT.

6) HELLISH DYSTOPIA: RIGHT-WING PERCEPTION OF COUNTRY IN WHICH PEOPLE HAVE INCREASED ACCESS TO HEALTH CARE.

WHEN PRE-EXISTING CONDITIONS ARE *OUTLAWED*--

--ONLY *OUTLAWS* WILL HAVE PRE-EXISTING CONDITIONS!

7) THE INHERENT FRAGILITY OF HUMAN EXISTENCE: CONCEPT WITH WHICH OPPONENTS OF HEALTH CARE REFORM ARE SEEMINGLY UNFAMILIAR.

I DON'T HAVE ANY HEALTH PROBLEMS, AT THIS PRECISE MOMENT!

IF *I* GET SICK, I'LL JUST HAVE A *BAKE SALE!*

OR TRADE SOME *CHICKENS!*

TOM TOMORROW © 2012...www.thismodernworld.com...twitter.com/tomtomorrow

THIS MODERN WORLD

by TOM TOMORROW

THIS WEEK: YOUR CORPORATE DEMOCRACY

FEATURING YOUR HOST **THE INVISIBLE HAND**

IF YOU'RE INVISIBLE, WHY CAN I **SEE** YOU?

UNLESS YOU'RE EXCEEDINGLY WEALTHY, NO ONE **CARES** WHAT YOU CAN SEE.

FOLKS, THERE'S ALWAYS BEEN A FUNDAMENTAL TENSION BETWEEN **CAPITALISM** AND **DEMOCRACY**.

WELL--TENSION **RESOLVED!**

WE HAVE A **WINNER!**

IT'S NOT YOU.

AS THE SUPREME COURT HAS RE-PEATEDLY MADE CLEAR--THIS COUNTRY **IS** FOR SALE TO THE HIGHEST BIDDER! MONEY **IS** SPEECH! CORPORATIONS **ARE** PEOPLE, MY FRIEND!

AND IF THAT **WASN'T** THE INTENT OF THE FOUNDING FATHERS--

--IT IS NOW.

MOVING FORWARD--WE'LL BE **STREAMLINING** SOME THINGS AROUND HERE! TAKE **ELECTIONS**--THEY'RE **SUCH** AN INEFFICIENT WAY TO PURCHASE A GOVERNMENT!

THAT'S WHY WE'LL BE REPLACING THEM WITH **EBAY AUCTIONS!** SIMPLE AND STRAIGHTFORWARD--HIGHEST BIDDER **WINS!**

YOU PROBABLY WON'T EVEN NOTICE THE DIFFERENCE.

WE'LL ALSO BE ELIMINATING MORE **REGULATIONS**--SLASHING UPPER INCOME **TAX RATES**--UNDERMINING **UNIONS**--YOU KNOW, THE USUAL STUFF.

OH, AND CRITICIZING THE SO-CALLED "ONE PERCENT" WILL SOON BE A **CRIMINAL OFFENSE.**

JOB CREATORS ARE **VERY** SENSITIVE PEOPLE.

OF COURSE, IF YOU DON'T **LIKE** ANY OF IT--YOU'RE ALWAYS FREE TO BUY YOUR **OWN** DEMOCRACY!

IF YOU CAN **AFFORD** IT.

HEH HEH.

REMEMBER--THE RICH AND POOR ARE EQUALLY FREE TO SLEEP UNDER BRIDGES!

UNLESS A RICH GUY WANTS YOUR SPOT.

THIS MODERN WORLD

by TOM TOMORROW

REPUBLICAN JU-JITSU

THEY LONG AGO MASTERED THE ART OF TURNING A RIVAL'S **STRENGTH** INTO A **WEAKNESS**.

I AM NOT GOING TO EXPLOIT, FOR POLITICAL PURPOSES, MY OPPONENT'S **LACK** OF EARLY-STAGE ALZHEIMER'S!

?!

IN 2004, THE BUSH CAMPAIGN NEUTRALIZED JOHN KERRY'S WAR RECORD WITH **BREATHTAKING** CHUTZPAH.

HA HA HA! JOHN KERRY GOT A "PURPLE HEART" IN "VIETNAM"!

OH, THE POOR WIDDLE BABY! DID HE STUB HIS **TOE** OR SOMETHING?

AND AFTER THE MOST INARTICULATE PRESIDENT IN AMERICAN HISTORY LEFT OFFICE, REPUBLICANS TRIED TO MAKE **TELEPROMPTERS** AN ISSUE FOR HIS SUCCESSOR.

DO YOU MEAN TO TELL ME THAT OBAMA IS JUST **READING** THOSE WORDS HE SAYS OFF OF SOME SORT OF **SCREEN**?

I AM **SHOCKED** TO LEARN OF THIS DECEPTIVE TECHNIQUE WHICH NO OTHER POLITICIAN HAS EVER UTILIZED!

BUT--AS WITH SO MANY THINGS-- THEIR CURRENT NOMINEE CAN'T QUITE SEEM TO GET THE **HANG** OF IT--

MITT ROMNEY OUTSOURCED AMERICAN JOBS DURING HIS TENURE AT BAIN CAPITAL!

BARACK **OBAMA** OUTSOURCED AMERICAN JOBS DURING **HIS** TENURE AT BAIN CAPITAL!

WAIT, WHAT?

--OPTING INSTEAD FOR THE MORE STRAIGHTFORWARD "I'M RUBBER, YOU'RE **GLUE**" STRATEGY.

MY OPPONENT NEEDS TO RELEASE HIS TAX RECORDS--AND CLARIFY EXACTLY WHEN HE **LEFT** BAIN!

MY OPPONENT NEEDS TO RELEASE **HIS** TAX RECORDS--AND CLARIFY WHEN **HE** LEFT BAIN!

YOU REALLY HAVE TO STOP THAT.

YOU REALLY HAVE TO STOP THAT!

HOW FAR HE'LL GO WITH THAT IS ANYBODY'S GUESS.

--AND IF YOU ASK **ME**, BARACK OBAMA IS THE **REAL** MORMON FORMER GOVERNOR OF MASSACHUSETTS AND SON OF GEORGE ROMNEY IN **THIS** RACE!

GOTTA LOVE THAT THICK, LUSTROUS HEAD OF **HAIR**, THOUGH!

AH, MITTENS-- A **WORD**, PLEASE...?

TOM TOMORROW ©2012....www.thismodernworld.com....twitter.com/tomtomorrow

THIS MODERN WORLD

by TOM TOMORROW

BOXED IN

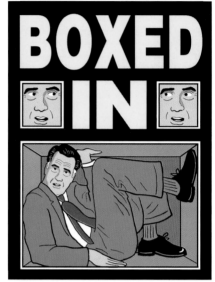

HE CAN'T MENTION HIS RECORD AS GOVERNOR.

MASSACHUSETTS, YOU SAY? HMM--THAT DOES SOUND *VAGUELY* FAMILIAR...

BUT I DO NOT KNOW THIS "*ROM-NEE-CARE*" OF WHICH YOU SPEAK.

HE'S AFRAID HIS RELIGION WILL ALIENATE FUNDAMENTALIST VOTERS.

LET'S JUST SAY I'M A MAN OF *FAITH*--

--AND QUICKLY CHANGE THE SUBJECT.

HEY, LOOK OVER THERE! IT'S AN OBAMA *TAX HIKE!*

HE CLEARLY DOESN'T BELIEVE IN FINANCIAL TRANSPARENCY.

CALL ME OLD-FASHIONED--BUT *I* HAPPEN TO BELIEVE THE METHODS BY WHICH AN INCOMPREHENSIBLY WEALTHY PRESIDENTIAL CANDIDATE AVOIDS TAXES ARE NOBODY'S BUSINESS BUT HIS *OWN!*

IT'S A MATTER OF *PRIN-CIPLE!*

AND HIS TIME AT BAIN IS OBVIOUS-LY A PROBLEM.

I AM QUALIFIED TO BE PRESIDENT BECAUSE OF MY *BUSINESS EX-PERIENCE*--

--WHICH IT IS *UNCONSCIONABLE* OF MY OPPONENT TO BRING UP!

HAVE YOU NO SENSE OF *DECENCY,* SIR?

MITT ROMNEY: DESPERATELY IN SEARCH OF SOMETHING HE *CAN* TALK ABOUT.

VOTE FOR ME BECAUSE--UM--I LIKE *PUPPIES!*

IS THAT WHY YOU TIED YOUR DOG TO THE ROOF OF YOUR CAR?

D'OH! I MEANT KITTENS! *KITTENS!!*

TOM TOMORROW © 2012...www.thismodernworld.com...twitter.com/tomtomorrow

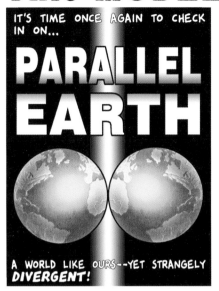

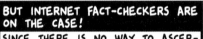

THIS MODERN WORLD

by TOM TOMORROW

WELCOME TO THE TICKET, SON! I'M SURE YOUR **BOLD IDEAS** WILL REALLY FIRE UP THE BASE--**AND** HELP DISTRACT ATTENTION FROM MY **TAX RETURNS!**

UH--WHO'S YOUR SLIGHTLY TRANS-LUCENT FRIEND?

OH, ER, UM--

--WELL, THIS IS THE **GHOST** OF **AYN RAND!** I KNOW YOUR STAFF TOLD ME TO **DISTANCE** MYSELF-- BUT I HAVEN'T BEEN ABLE TO **SHAKE** HER!

SHAKE **ME?** YOU COL-LECTIVIST **PAWN!** YOU ARE **UNWORTHY** OF MY IMPARTED WISDOM!

BUT WHAT SHOULD I HAVE **EX-PECTED**--FROM A WEAK-WILLED GOD-BELIEVER WHO USED **SOCIAL SECURITY SURVIVOR BENEFITS** TO PAY FOR COLLEGE--LIKE ANY COMMON, UNDESERVING **MOOCHER!**

HEY! **YOU** TOOK SOCIAL SECURITY-- **AND** MEDICARE-- WHEN YOU GOT SICK!

DON'T CHANGE THE SUBJECT, MOOCHER!

LOOK--I WANT TO CUT TAXES FOR THE WEALTHY! I WANT TO SLASH SOCIAL WELFARE PROGRAMS! I WANT TO LIBERATE SELF-RELIANT ACHIEVERS FROM THE DEMANDS OF THE WEAK AND PARASITICAL!

I WANT TO SHAPE SOCIETY AFTER **YOUR** VISION!

BAH! YOU **DISGUST** ME!

YOU OPPOSE ABORTION--AND THERE-FORE, THE RIGHTS OF THE **INDI-VIDUAL!** YOU'RE JUST ANOTHER CONTEMPTIBLE CLOSET **STATIST**-- LIKE **RONALD REAGAN!** I URGED MY FOLLOWERS NOT TO VOTE FOR **HIM**, YOU KNOW!

I DESPISE YOUR KIND--WITH **RATIONAL OBJECTIVITY!**

REAL RAY OF SUNSHINE YOU GOT THERE. YOU SAY YOU TWO ARE **INSEPARABLE?**

WELL, YEAH-- BUT MOSTLY PEOPLE DON'T SEEM TO **NOTICE.**

THEIR **LOSS,** THE WEAK-MINDED **FOOLS.**

NEXT: THE GHOST OF **ST. THOMAS AQUINAS!**

YOU--YOU KNOW **NOTH-ING** OF MY WORK!

D'OH!

TOM TOMORROW ©2012....www.thismodernworld.com....twitter.com/tomtomorrow

THIS MODERN WORLD

by TOM TOMORROW

THE INVADERS

STRANGE VISITORS FROM A DISTANT, BARREN PLANET!

WE MUST REPLENISH OUR POPULATION--OR OUR SPECIES IS *DOOMED!*

FORTUNATELY OUR SCANS INDICATE THE FEMALES OF *EARTH* WILL MAKE *EXCELLENT* BREEDING STOCK!

UH--OKAY THEN! PLOT US A *COURSE!*

I ALREADY HAVE, SIR.

THEY HAVE A DEVIOUS PLAN.

WE WILL INFILTRATE THEIR POLITICAL SYSTEM--AND *ABOLISH* THE SO-CALLED "RIGHT" TO TERMINATE UNWANTED PREGNANCIES!

AND *THEN*--WE ACTIVATE THE *REMOTE MASS IMPREGNATION DEVICE*--

--AND *INVADE* THE UTERUSES OF PLANET EARTH!

THINGS PROCEED SMOOTHLY--UNTIL THE INVADER KNOWN AS *TODD AKIN* SAYS TOO *MUCH!*

IT IS *MY* UNDERSTANDING THAT HUMAN FEMALES DO NOT BECOME PREGNANT THROUGH "LEGITIMATE RAPE."

THOUGH ADMITTEDLY I AM NOT A XENOBIOLOGIST.

SAY WHAT?

THE ALIEN COLLECTIVE BEGS HIM TO SACRIFICE HIMSELF FOR THE GREATER GOOD.

YOU *FOOL!* YOU MUST VOLUNTARILY SELF-DISCORPORATE--OR YOU WILL EXPOSE US *ALL!*

RELAX! THE HUMANS WILL FORGET ALL ABOUT IT, WITHIN ONE OR TWO OF THEIR "NEWS CYCLES."

FAILING THAT, THEY TRY TO DISTANCE THEMSELVES FROM THEIR FORMER COMRADE.

WE DISAPPROVE OF THE FORCED IMPREGNATION OF HUMAN FEMALES! *DON'T* WE, PAUL RYAN?

ER--*YES!* WE *DEFINITELY* DO NOT VIEW EARTHWOMEN AS DISPOSABLE *BREEDING STOCK!*

NONETHELESS--SOME HUMANS BEGIN TO SUSPECT SOMETHING IS *AMISS.*

REPUBLICANS ARE *PANICKING* ABOUT THIS! THEY MUST REALIZE THAT THEIR EXTREMIST VIEWS WILL *ALIENATE* VOTERS!

YES...I'M SURE THAT'S IT... WHAT OTHER EXPLANATION COULD THERE *BE*...?

TO BE *CONTINUED*...

TOM TOMORROW © 2012....www.thismodernworld.com...twitter.com/tomtomorrow

endnotes

The publishers and I thought it might be useful to provide additional (if subjective) context for some of the topical references in these cartoons. Endnotes are numbered by page. The date at the beginning of each endnote indicates the initial week of publication for that cartoon. Endnotes without additional text indicate a cartoon that seemed sufficiently self-explanatory.

1. **08-11-2010.**

2. **08-25-2010.** The so-called "Ground Zero Mosque" was an Islamic community center proposed for a site two blocks away from Ground Zero. Hysteria about the project was whipped up by right-wing bloggers and politicians who professed shock at the alleged defilement of sacred ground, i.e. an old Burlington Coat Factory in a neighborhood full of strip clubs, OTB parlors and fast food joints.

3. **09-01-2010.**

4. **09-08-2010.** Judging people not "by the color of their skin but by the content of their character," is apparently the only MLK quote with which right-wingers are familiar.

5. **09-15-2010.** I find it strange that in the twenty-first century, we still require our candidates for higher office to profess their belief in invisible, imaginary beings.

6. **09-22-2010.** The *New Yorker* article mentioned in the title panel was written by Jane Mayer. It was an in-depth look at the billionaire Koch brothers and their stealth support for the Tea Party, which up to that point had been largely portrayed in the media as a spontaneous grass-roots movement.

7. **09-29-2010.** Newt Gingrich had recently given a speech in which he warned of "stealth jihadis" who were seeking to "replace Western civilization with a radical imposition of Sharia." He went on to castigate the left for not responding more proactively to these imaginary menaces, accusing secular elites of "appeasement" and observing, "How we don't have some kind of movement in this country on the left that understands that Sharia is a direct mortal threat to virtually every value that the left has is really one of the most interesting historical questions and will someday lead to many dissertations being written."

8. **10-06-2010.** I generally wouldn't have done two Conservative Jones cartoons in a row, but a breaking news story proved irresistible. Breitbart protege James O'Keefe, of the famously misleading ACORN "sting," had agreed to an interview with CNN reporter Abbie Boudreau for a documentary on conservative activism. O'Keefe actually planned to lure her aboard a boat stocked with sex toys and porn, where he planned to "seduce" her in front of hidden cameras. CNN obtained the planning document prepared by O'Keefe and his collaborators. According to an online CBS news report:

> The "CNN Caper" document laid out a message that O'Keefe would record in advance of the prank in which he would complain that CNN was planning "to portray me and my friends as crazies, as non-journalists, as unprofessional and likely as homophobes, racists or bigots of some sort."

> For that reason, the script continued, O'Keefe would say, "I'm going to punk CNN. Abbie has been trying to seduce me to use me, in order to spin a lie about me. So, I'm going to seduce her, on camera, to use her for a video. This bubble-headed-bleach-blonde who comes on at five will get a taste of her own medicine, she'll get seduced on camera and you'll get to see the awkwardness and the aftermath."

That had Conservative Jones written all over it, particularly in light of the list of props, which read like a fourteen-year-old boy's concept of seduction: strawberries, champagne, dildos, a ceiling mirror, posters and paintings of naked women, copies of *Playboy* and other pornographic magazines, Viagra pills, fuzzy handcuffs and a blindfold.

The bizarre scheme collapsed when one of O'Keefe's collaborators came to her senses and warned the reporter off.

9. **10-13-2010.** Tea Party activists portrayed in the second and third panels of this cartoon are, from left to right: Sen. Rand Paul, (losing) Senate candidates Joe Miller, Ken Buck and Sharron Angle, and Sen. Jim DeMint. The fourth panel mentions (losing) Senate candidate Christine O'Donnell, who had previously made a name for herself preaching the evils of masturbation, and who once told Bill Maher she had "dabbled in witchcraft" (eventually necessitating the famous "I'm not a witch" ad). The final panel refers to the fight Obama surrogates picked with "the professional left" and critical left-wing bloggers, blaming them for the so-called progressive enthusiasm gap of the 2010 midterms.

10. **10-20-2010.** This cartoon was based on the true story of a Florida man who had paid cash for his house, and therefore had no mortgage—a technicality which did not stop Bank of America from attempting to foreclose his home. (After the case received widespread publicity, BofA acknowledged the error and rescinded the foreclosure.)

11. **10-27-2010.** Carl Paladino was the (losing) Tea Party-favored candidate for Governor of New York in 2010, best remembered for forwarding a series of racist and sexually explicit emails; threatening a reporter from the *New York Post* (telling him "I'll take you out"); and for having fathered a child in an extramarital relationship. He also declared that Obama's health care reform would kill more people than 9/11. The guy "who likes to dress up like a Nazi" was Rich Iott, a (losing) Tea Party-favored House candidate from Ohio and historical re-enactor.

12. **11-03-2010.**

13. **11-10-2010.** In the 2010 midterms, Republicans gained 63 seats in the House (recapturing the majority), and six seats in the Senate.

14. **11-17-2010.** The Simpson-Bowles Commission was widely referred to on left-wing blogs as the "Catfood Commission," a reference to its focus on cutting entitlements for the elderly and needy. Hard-core Obama supporters would later explain that Obama formed the bipartisan commission in order to explicitly *not* follow its recommendations, apparently as one of the eleventh-dimension-chess strategies often attributed to him by said supporters.

15. **11-24-2010.** The TSA was rolling out its new full-body scanners, made by Rapiscan (which Stephen Colbert told his audience he hoped was not pronounced "rape-i-scan"). The FDA and TSA assured the public the backscatter radiation used by the scanners was perfectly safe; critics argued that the agencies were glossing over the dangers. A side note: the lead lobbyist for Rapiscan was (and apparently still is) Michael Chertoff, the heavily-criticized former head of Homeland Security.

16. **12-01-2010.**

17. **12-08-2010.** Anyone who's ever been to a flea market knows that you don't open with your best offer. The ongoing budget battles made it clear that Obama was entirely unfamiliar with this basic rule of negotiation.

18. **12-15-2010.**

19. **01-05-2011.**

20. **12-22-2010.** The Year in Review (or in this case, Year in Crazy) cartoons have become a yearly *TMW* tradition, as well as a way to work up a couple of cartoons in advance so that I can take the holidays off like a normal person.

Panel six (Feb. 16): this refers to the assertion of Frank Gaffney (a protege of Richard Perle) that the logo for the Missile Defense Agency deliberately incorporated an Islamic crescent. A few months later, as noted in the April 14 panel, right-wingers theorized that the Nuclear Security Summit logo was also deliberately invoking said crescent.

Panel thirteen (May 21): in 2008, the Supreme Court, in *Boumediene v. Bush*, held that constitutional rights to habeas corpus applied even to foreign nationals held at Guantanamo (a decision praised at the time by candidate Obama). The Bush administration then argued that *Boumediene* did not apply to detainees held at Bagram, an argument subsequently adopted by the

Obama Department of Justice. On May 21, 2010, the DC Circuit Court of Appeals adopted the Bush/Obama argument that detainees held at Bagram rather than Gitmo had no right of appeal.

Panel fourteen (June 6): Elton John was reportedly paid one million dollars to sing at gay-marriage-opponent Rush Limbaugh's fourth attempt at traditional marriage.

21. **12-29-2010.** Panel three (July 20): Shirley Sherrod was forced to resign from her regional position with the USDA after Andrew Breitbart released video excerpts from a speech making it appear that she had treated a white farmer with racial animosity. The unedited video put the anecdote in context and made it clear that she was actually making the opposite point. Oddly, it was Glenn Beck who first exposed the deceit, on his Fox News show, leading to a falling out between Breitbart and Beck.

Panel seven (Sept. 8): the US Court of Appeals for the 9th Circuit dismissed a lawsuit brought by the ACLU on behalf of a victim of extraordinary rendition, upholding the Obama administration's invocation of state secrets. Democrats who would have been outraged by the same news during the Bush administration were largely indifferent.

22. **01-12-2011.** This cartoon was written after gunman Jared Loughner's shooting rampage, which left six people dead, severely wounded Congresswoman Gabrielle Giffords, and immediately set off the usual debate about whether or not guns kill people.

23. **01-12-2011.** On July 18, 2010, California Highway Patrol officers stopped an erratic driver, leading to a shootout with the man, who was heavily armed and wearing body armor. He told investigators he wanted "to start a revolution" by "killing people of importance at the Tides Foundation and the ACLU." The shooter would later acknowledge that his thwarted killing spree had been inspired by Beck's frequent tirades against both organizations.

24. **01-26-2011.** Cartoon loosely inspired by the Pearl Jam song "Unthought Known," on the album *Backspacer* (for which I did the cover art).

The middle third of the first panel is a reference to unexplained mass death of birds and fish, several instances of which were reported in early 2011.

The poster in the background of the final panel is a nod to John Carpenter's classic horror/sci fi/political satire, *They Live*.

25. **02-02-2011.** This was written in response to the Glenn Beck/Tea Party tendency to deify the Founding Fathers without seeming entirely clear on what exactly they did or stood for. Michele Bachmann declared that the Founders—many of whom were slave owners—"worked tirelessly until slavery was no more in the United States." She singled out John Quincy Adams for praise, leading her defenders to argue that a man born in 1767 did, in fact, qualify as a Founding Father. George Soros and Frances Fox Piven were (and remain) major *bêtes noires* of the Tea Party right—the

former for being rich and sometimes supporting liberal causes, the latter for co-authoring an article in *The Nation* in 1966 which must have been read by literally tens of people, and which Tea Partiers nonetheless believe to be one of the foundational documents of the Vast Left Wing Conspiracy. (Both Soros and Piven were frequently demonized at the time by Beck and his now-mostly-forgotten blackboards).

26. **02-09-2011.** According to an 04-05-2003 account in the *New York Times,* American troops were greeted as liberators by an enthusiastic Iraqi who told a reporter that he hoped they would bring "democracy, whiskey and sexy." Triumphant right-wing bloggers immediately made this their new catchphrase for a rapid, unambiguous victory in Iraq, which was at that time seen as a foregone conclusion.

27. **02-16-2011.** If this cartoon seems slightly disjointed, it's because it was written over the course of a weekend as the events of the Egyptian uprising were unfolding. At first it looked as if Mubarek would be handing power over to Omar Suleiman, an army general who was the CIA's point man on extraordinary rendition, portrayed here as the Dungeon Master. The fifth panel's "whoops! Change of plans!" reflects both the rapidly-evolving news from Egypt that weekend and the process of writing the cartoon in real time.

28. **02-23-2011.** Writing in *Mother Jones* in January 2011, Nick Baumann explained why Republicans tried to redefine rape:

For years, federal laws restricting the use of government funds to pay for abortions have included exemptions for pregnancies resulting from rape or incest. (Another exemption covers pregnancies that could endanger the life of the woman.) But the "No Taxpayer Funding for Abortion Act," a bill with 173 mostly Republican co-sponsors that House Speaker John Boehner (R-Ohio) has dubbed a top priority in the new Congress, contains a provision that would rewrite the rules to limit drastically the definition of rape and incest in these cases.

With this legislation, which was introduced last week by Rep. Chris Smith (R-N.J.), Republicans propose that the rape exemption be limited to "forcible rape." This would rule out federal assistance for abortions in many rape cases, including instances of statutory rape, many of which are non-forcible. For example: If a 13-year-old girl is impregnated by a 24-year-old adult, she would no longer qualify to have Medicaid pay for an abortion.

Paul Ryan was one of the co-sponsors of the bill. After an onslaught of criticism, House Republicans removed the provision.

29. **03-02-2011.**

30. **03-09-2011.** This cartoon was intended as the Glox version of the striking (or "non-acquiesing") Wisconsin schoolteachers who tried, courageously but ultimately unsuccessfully, to defend collective bargaining rights from their Koch-fueled anti-union governor.

With that much in mind, the rest of it should be easier to interpret.

31. **03-16-2011.** I assume readers are familiar with the story of Bradley Manning, who leaked a trove of classified information to Wikileaks and was kept in harshly punitive confinement as a result. The "progressive fantasy" of Obama paraphrases something Obama said during the presidential campaign—that whistleblowing is an act of courage and patriotism, and should be encouraged rather than stifled.

32. **03-23-2011.**

33. **03-30-2011.** Obama's intervention in Libya threw right-wingers for a loop—in Conservative Jones's words, how to support bombs without supporting Obama? The story they eventually settled on was that Obama was only reacting to the incessant shrewish nagging of the women around him, specifically Hillary Clinton and Samantha Power.

34. **04-06-2011.** In April of 2011 a budget impasse very nearly led to the first government shutdown since the Gingrich debacle of the mid-nineties. Speaker of the House John Boehner found himself fighting a two-front war, against both Democrats and the radical Tea Party wing of his own party. In the end (and after the deadline for this cartoon), Democrats agreed to $38 billion in cuts.

35. **04-13-2011.** Inspired by Paul Ryan's budget plan, which Paul Krugman described at the time as "ludicrous and cruel":

And then there's the much-ballyhooed proposal to abolish Medicare and replace it with vouchers that can be used to buy private health insurance.

The point here is that privatizing Medicare does nothing, in itself, to limit health-care costs. In fact, it almost surely raises them by adding a layer of middlemen. Yet the House plan assumes that we can cut health-care spending as a percentage of G.D.P. despite an aging population and rising health care costs.

The only way that can happen is if those vouchers are worth much less than the cost of health insurance. In fact, the Congressional Budget Office estimates that by 2030 the value of a voucher would cover only a third of the cost of a private insurance policy equivalent to Medicare as we know it. So the plan would deprive many and probably most seniors of adequate health care.

36. **04-20-2011.** The thing to note about this cartoon is that it ran in April, 2011, several months before the Occupy Wall Street movement arose and the phrase "one percent" entered common usage as a synonym for great wealth. The numbers Sparky quotes actually underestimate the percentage of wealth owned by the very richest Americans in 2011, but they were the most recent numbers I could find at that moment.

37. **04-27-2011.** Libya didn't turn out to be the quagmire I feared, but that doesn't mean that Obama's actions were legal—as noted by

critics such as Glenn Greenwald and Yale Law professor Bruce Ackerman, as well as by candidate Obama, who declared in December 2007 that "the President does not have power under the Constitution to unilaterally authorize a military attack in a situation that does not involve stopping an actual or imminent threat to the nation."

38. **05-04-2011.** For a few days, while the presidential campaign was in the early silly-season stage, Donald Trump—who was still politely referred to as a "potential presidential candidate"—started making noise about Obama's birth certificate. Obama finally gave in and released the damn thing, trumping Trump and his birther conspiracies. A few days later it would all be overshadowed by the news that Osama bin Laden had been killed.

39. **05-11-2011.**

40. **05-18-2011.**

41. **05-25-2011.** Another one on Obama's war on whistleblowers (see endnote 31 above). As this cartoon notes (citing an article by Jane Mayer in the 05-23-2011 issue of *The New Yorker),* the administration has invoked the Espionage Act more times than all previous administrations combined.

42. **06-01-2011.**

43. **06-08-2011.** Senators Ron Wyden and Mark Udall are on the Senate Intelligence Committee, and actually know the classified uses to which the Patriot Act is being put—and while clearly constrained by the restrictions of their security clearances, they've been trying to warn the public that there's cause for concern. During a reauthorization debate in late May, 2011 Wyden stated: "I want to deliver a warning this afternoon: When the American people find out how their government has secretly interpreted the Patriot Act, they will be stunned and they will be angry...It's almost as if there are two Patriot Acts, and many members of Congress haven't even read the one that matters. Our constituents, of course, are totally in the dark. Members of the public have no access to the executive branch's secret legal interpretations, so they have no idea what their government thinks this law means." Udall echoed, "Americans would be alarmed if they knew how this law is being carried out."

44. **06-15-2011.** In the first truly postmodern sex scandal of the Twitter era, Congressman Anthony Weiner hit the wrong button on his phone and accidentally shared a picture of the shape of his penis (beneath his underpants) with all of his Twitter followers, rather than the young woman for whom it was intended. Before he was able to delete it, somebody grabbed a screen shot and sent it to Andrew Breitbart. Weiner tried to deny ownership of the penis-shape, but ultimately was forced to resign, while Breitbart, for once, managed to break a scandal based on neither lies nor deceptive editing. (Such was Breitbart's legacy that when news of his untimely death broke less than a year later, many people—myself included—wondered if it was yet another deception, perhaps to lure liberal commentators into saying something ungenerous for which they could be denounced.)

45. **06-22-2011.**

46. **06-29-2011.** Libya again (see endnotes 33 and 37, above). At this point, Obama's surrogates were arguing that the war in Libya was not subject to the War Powers Act deadline for seeking Congressional approval because it was not a war at all, but rather a "kinetic military action." As noted in the cartoon, Obama's own top legal advisors disagreed with this conclusion, but were overruled.

47. **07-06-2011.** A dystopian cartoon written a few weeks earlier, while jet-lagged in the middle of the night in a hotel room in Perugia, Italy (where I was a speaker at the International Journalism Festival).

48. **07-13-2011.** The Glox News version of the budget showdown.

49. **07-20-2011.** As the *New York Times* explains, "Federal law requires Congress to authorize the government to borrow any money that is needed to pay for the programs that Congress has passed." In other words, raising the debt ceiling means Congress agrees to pay off debts that have *already been incurred.* This was largely considered a formality until the Republicans took control of the House in 2010. Whether as a result of strategy or ignorance (Michele Bachmann seemed to believe that the national debt was increased *as a result* of raising the debt ceiling), Tea Party Republicans decided this was a battleground on which to make their stand. Obama, for his part, could have made raising the debt ceiling a condition for extending the Bush tax cuts the previous December, but chose not to, explaining:

"Look, here's my expectation—and I'll take John Boehner at his word—that nobody, Democrat or Republican, is willing to see the full faith and credit of the United States government collapse, that that would not be a good thing to happen. And so I think that there will be significant discussions about the debt limit vote. That's something that nobody ever likes to vote on. But once John Boehner is sworn in as Speaker, then he's going to have responsibilities to govern. You can't just stand on the sidelines and be a bomb thrower."

Obama also made it clear during the negotiations that he was willing to offer up cuts to Social Security and Medicare in his quest for a bipartisan Grand Bargain, chastising Democrats who would "prefer not to have to do anything on entitlements, would prefer frankly not to do anything on these debt and deficit problems." As far as I can tell, the only thing that kept the programs off the chopping block (for the moment) was Tea Party intransigence—they weren't smart enough to take what the president was offering them on a silver platter.

50. **07-27-2011.**

51. **08-03-2011.** Regular readers of Thomas Friedman's tortured prose know that he is obsessed with the formation of a third party similar to Democrats in almost every respect, but with a smidgen more emphasis on debt reduction. His 07-23-2011 column breathlessly praised the latest such effort, Americans Elect, "a quiet political start-up that is now ready to show its hand, a viable, centrist, third presidential ticket."

He confidently declared, "What Amazon.com did to books, what the blogosphere did to newspapers, what the iPod did to music, what drugstore.com did to pharmacies, Americans Elect plans to do to the two-party duopoly that has dominated American political life: remove the barriers to real competition, flatten the incumbents and let the people in. Watch out." As is almost always the case, Friedman was laughably wrong—Americans Elect folded the $35 million effort the following May due to an almost universal lack of interest.

52. **08-10-2011.** The debt ceiling crisis was ultimately resolved with an agreement to create a bipartisan super committee tasked with drastically reducing the federal deficit. If the committee failed to cut at least $1.2 trillion by November, that amount would automatically be cut from domestic and defense budgets, theoretically spreading the pain equally between Democrats and Republicans. Of course the effort failed, and as of this writing the automatic cuts are scheduled to help push the nation over what is being termed the "fiscal cliff" at the end of 2012.

53. **08-17-2011.** As discussed above in endnote 49, Tea Partiers did not always seem to grasp the implications of the debt ceiling battle, leading to a rift with the more mainstream, Wall Street wing of the Republican party.

54. **08-24-2011.**

55. **09-07-2011.**

56. **09-14-2011.** The alien political scientist was intended as a reboot of a character from *TMW* from the early

nineties, which was in turn based on the *Weekly World News* alien who visited Earth to meet with various presidential candidates (if that one was before your time, Google it). So far I've only used him twice, and I'm not really sure if he'll be sticking around or not.

57. **09-21-2011.** A sequel to a previous cartoon from 2005, in which the same car drives off the same cliff.

58. **09-28-2011.** Pushing the ultimately unsuccessful American Jobs Act, Obama abandoned his usual bipartisan demeanor in favor of slightly more populist rhetoric—much to the dismay of David Brooks, who declared (more-in-sorrow-than-anger), "Yes, I'm a sap. I believed Obama when he said he wanted to move beyond the stale ideological debates that have paralyzed this country. I always believe that Obama is on the verge of breaking out of the conventional categories and embracing one of the many bipartisan reform packages that are floating around." The Republican primaries were underway at the same time, hence the cameo from momentary front-runner Rick Perry at the end of the cartoon.

59. **10-05-2011.** Repubicans were blaming Obama for rising gas prices. Bachmann promised that if she were elected, she would bring the price of gasoline down below $2 a gallon. Since the price of gas is determined by the global crude oil market, it was anyone's guess how she would achieve this.

Dr. Von Philbert's invention is, of course, a nod to the 1960s Irwin Allen sci-fi program, *The Time Tunnel*.

60. **10-12-2011.**

61. **10-19-2011.** IHOTFM-Man's plan is based on David Brooks' 10-10-2011 column, "The Milquetoast Radicals," which declared that "The 99-versus-1 frame is also extremely self-limiting. If you think all problems flow from a small sliver of American society, then all your solutions are going to be small, too, " before concluding that "moderates in suits are much more radical than the pierced anarchists camping out on Wall Street."

62. **10-26-2011.** The Heritage Foundation had released a paper earlier in the year which argued that the poor in America aren't really poor because they have cellphones and so on—a perennial right-wing canard that seems to resurface every few years.

63. **11-02-2011.**

64. **11-09-2011.**

65. **11-16-2011.** Not Mitt Romney was inspired by a joke someone made on a listserv I was on, as well as by Bil Keane's recurrent "Not Me" character from *The Family Circus*.

66. **11-23-2011.** The absurd charade of Herman Cain's presidential candidacy began to unravel as reports of sexual harassment started surfacing, leading to much regrettable commentary from conservatives about the women involved and their imagined motivations.

67. **11-30-2011.**

68. **12-07-2011.**

69. **12-14-2011.** For those of us who were paying attention to politics in the nineties, it was surreal to watch Newt Gingrich being taken seriously as a presidential contender, however briefly.

70. **12-21-2011.** Panel two, "redefining rape"—see endnote 28, above. Panel fourteen (May 26): Wyden & Udall—see endnote 43, above.

71. **12-28-2011.** Panel four (Sept. 12): Wolf Blitzer asked Ron Paul a question about a hypothetical healthy 30-year-old without health insurance who suddenly comes down sick. The ensuing exchange is from the transcript:

> PAUL: He should do whatever he wants to do, and assume responsibility for himself. My advice to him would be have a major medical policy. But not forced—
>
> BLITZER: But he doesn't have that. And he needs intensive care for six months. Who pays?
>
> PAUL: That's what freedom is all about. Taking your own risks. This whole idea that you have to prepare to take care of everybody.
>
> BLITZER: But congressman, are you saying that society should just let him die?
>
> CROWD: [Yeah! Yeah! Laughs.]

(The crowd at a previous Republican debate had already broken into spontaneous applause and cheers after moderator Brian Williams noted that as governor Rick Perry had "executed 234 death row inmates, more than any other governor in modern times.")

Ron Paul's 2008 campaign manager, Kent Snyder, died that same year from pneumonia. He lacked insurance due to a pre-existing condition, leaving a $400,000 medical bill which was passed on to his mother. An online fund was set up to help her, though it's unclear how much money was raised—according to Talking Points Memo, the site stopped updating in 2008 with only $34,870 in donations.

Fifth panel (Sept. 22): Appearing via YouTube video, an openly gay soldier addressed a question to Rick Santorum: "In 2010, when I was deployed to Iraq, I had to lie about who I was, because I'm a gay soldier, and I didn't want to lose my job. My question is, under one of your presidencies, do you intend to circumvent the progress that's been made for gay and lesbian soldiers in the military?" The crowd booed him.

Sixth panel (Sept. 24): Whimsically-named NYPD officer Anthony Bologna was caught on video approaching a group of women corralled by orange netting and casually pepper-spraying them without warning. This is not to be confused with the incident at UC Davis, in which Lt. John Pike was caught on video casually pepper-spraying sitting demonstrators. (The image of Pike and his pepper spray became an instant meme online.) In August, 2012 it was announced that the police chief at UC Davis had overruled an internal affairs recommendation and fired Pike.

Eighth panel (Sept. 30): Al Qaeda propagandist and U.S. citizen Anwar al-Awlaki was killed in a drone strike, setting off a debate as to whether the President of the United States has the constitutional authority to assassinate U.S. citizens abroad. Most of Obama's supporters seemed to agree it was okay because al-Awlaki was a terrorist. Less attention was paid to the death of his 16-year-old son, also a U.S. citizen, who was killed in an airstrike a few weeks later.

72. **01-04-2012.**

73. **01-11-2012.**

74. **01-18-2012.** In a pre-internet era I might have taken the "Romdroid" idea and run with it for the rest of the campaign, but I hate doing the same joke that everyone else is doing, and comparisons of Romney to a robot quickly became so commonplace as to be banal.

When this cartoon was written, some of the harshest criticism of Romney was coming from Newt Gingrich, hence his appearance in the final panel.

75. **01-25-2012.** According to the ACLU:

> On December 31, 2011, President Obama signed the National Defense Authorization Act (NDAA), codifying indefinite military detention without charge or trial into law for the first time in American history. The NDAA's dangerous detention provisions would authorize the president—and all future presidents—to order the military to pick up and indefinitely imprison people captured anywhere in the world, far from any battlefield.

A side note about this one: I'd just had a bedbug scare after a trip to Florida. Which just goes to show, you never know where inspiration is going to come from.

76. **02-01-2012.** Gingrich's demeanor during the debates could only be described as one of barely-contained contempt. He clearly felt he was the smartest man on stage, and seemed perpetually annoyed by the failure of others to acknowledge it.

Around this time, Gingrich told a crowd, "The fact is, if I become your nominee, we will make the key test very simple. Food stamps, versus pay checks. Obama is the best food stamp president in American history. More people are on food stamps today because of Obama's policies than ever in history. I would like to be the best paycheck president in American history."

To battle his growing reputation as an out-of-touch rich guy, Mitt Romney released a photograph of himself posing awkwardly in front of a washing machine, allegedly doing his own laundry on the campaign trail.

77. **02-08-2012.** Tea Party activists in Tennessee wanted textbooks to remove references to slavery or the fact that the Founding Fathers owned slaves. See also endnote 25, above.

Ever since Wall Street crashed the economy in 2008, right-wingers have been trying to blame the subprime meltdown on the 1977 Community Reinvestment Act, which required banks to lend in low-income neighborhoods where they took deposits. The problem is that most subprime loans were made by institutions not subject to the CRA. This hasn't stopped the right from creating a narrative in which poor people and minorities are the real culprits, rather than Wall Street bankers.

According to whoever tallies these things on the internet, George W. Bush took 967 vacation days—32% of his time in office. He was also not known for being an articulate impromptu speaker, to say the least. So of course the right wing tried to make an issue of *Obama's* vacations, and the fact that he uses a teleprompter when giving speeches, like every other president of the modern era.

78. **02-15-2012.**

79. **02-22-2012.** Rick Santorum made some news by stating in an interview:

> One of the things I will talk about that no president has talked about before is I think the dangers of contraception in this country, the whole sexual libertine idea... It's not okay because it's a license to do things in the sexual realm that is counter to how things are supposed to be. They're supposed to be within marriage, for purposes that are, yes, conjugal...but also procreative.
>
> That's the perfect way that a sexual union should happen. We take any part of that out, we diminish the act. And if you can take one part out that's not for purposes of procreation, that's not one of the reasons, then you diminish this very special bond between men and women, so why can't you take other parts of that out? And all of a sudden, it becomes deconstructed to the point where it's simply pleasure. And

that's certainly a part of it—and it's an important part of it, don't get me wrong—but there's a lot of things we do for pleasure, and this is special, and it needs to be seen as special. Again, I know most presidents don't talk about those things, and maybe people don't want us to talk about those things, but I think it's important that you are who you are. I'm not running for preacher.

I'm not running for pastor, but these are important public policy issues.

Anyone who doesn't understand why Santorum wouldn't want to be Googled need only Google his last name.

80. **02-29-2012.** Catholic priests objected to Obamacare because it would require religious employers to pay for women's health needs, including birth control and reproductive servies.

Virginia lawmakers wanted to mandate invasive, medically unnecessary transvaginal ultrasounds for women seeking abortions. At the time this cartoon was written, it appeared they had been forced to back down, but the bill was ultimately signed into law in March. Twenty other states have similar laws as of this writing.

81. **03-07-2012.** Rick Santorum experienced a surge in March as Republicans tried desperately to avoid nominating Mitt Romney.

Asked about Afghanistan, Newt Gingrich actually said, "And there are some problems where you have to say, 'You know, you are going to have to figure out how to live your own miserable life … because you clearly don't want to learn from me how to be unmiserable.' And that is what you are going to see happen."

Indiana GOP Rep. Bob Morris had recently denounced the Girl Scouts as "bent on promoting communism, lesbianism and subverting traditional American family values," while Fox News had accused the new *Muppets* movie of spreading a communist, anti-capitalist message.

82. **03-14-2012.** Eric Holder gave a speech allegedly laying out the legal case for targeted killing. Writing in *Slate*, legal analyst Emily Bazelon (who is, full disclosure, a friend) noted:

If you want to believe that the government does its grim best to fight terrorists, and you're inclined to think that their dirty tactics justify some ruthlessness on our part, then maybe a few killings of bad guys in faraway lands doesn't bother you much. But there are a couple of unsettling implications here that are so obvious that it's amazing Holder thinks he need not address them. The first is that if the Obama administration claims this kind of extra-judicial power for a few cases, what's to stop the next president from expanding upon it—and citing this step as precedent for taking others that Obama wouldn't countenance? And the second is that when the executive branch won't release the legal memos that underlie its decision-making, we're blocked from evaluating how strong or weak the arguments are. When the federal government takes a bold and new step like this, testing the boundaries of the Constitution, it's crucial for Holder and his lawyers to explain how and why. Instead, we're being asked to take the wisdom of the president and his national security apparatus for granted.

83. **03-21-2012.**

84. **03-28-2012.** On February 26, an unarmed black teenager named Trayvon Martin was shot by self-appointed neighborhood watchdog George Zimmerman. Florida police initially chose not to charge Zimmerman, due to Florida's "Stand Your Ground" self-defense law, leading to a national outcry.

85. **04-04-2012.** During the Supreme Court oral arguments over the Affordable Care Act, Justice Scalia asked the administration's lawyer, "Could you define the market—everybody has to buy food sooner or later, so you define the market as food, therefore, everybody is in the market; therefore, you can make people buy broccoli?"

86. **04-11-2012.** Goofball and Galahad are of course based on Goofus and Gallant from the doctor's-office staple, *Highlights for Children*.

87. **04-18-2012.** On April 2, the Supreme Court ruled that officials can strip search anyone arrested for any offense, no matter how minor, before admitting them into the general jail population. Less noted by liberal critics was the fact that the Obama DOJ had formally urged the Court to reach that conclusion.

88. **04-25-2012.** Blueprints for the rennovation of Romney's La Jolla

beach house had been leaked to the press, revealing plans for a car elevator for the garage. Meanwhile an old interview with Ann Romney surfaced, in which she explained how, as a struggling young couple, she and Mitt were able to make ends meet "because Mitt had enough of an investment from stock that we could sell off a little at a time."

On April 17, Newt Gingrich was bitten by a penguin at the St. Louis Zoo, and I clearly couldn't let that pass without acknowledgement.

89. **05-02-2012.** An anti-abortion group attempted an O'Keefe-style sting on Planned Parenthood. Clinics in eleven states reported "patients" coming in to ask about the gender of their fetus, and whether they could terminate the pregnancy if the baby was a girl.

90. **05-09-2012.** See endnote 43 on Wyden and Udall, and endnote 82 on Holder, both above.

91. **05-16-2012.** Paul Krugman makes a cameo in the fourth panel.

92. **05-23-2012.** Aiming for the domestic police market, manufacturers are offering drones which can be mounted with grenade launchers and/or 12-gauge shotguns.

93. **05-30-2012.** The "internal deliberations" line comes from an article in the 05-29-2012 edition of the *New York Times*:

> That record, and Mr. Awlaki's calls for more attacks, presented Mr. Obama with an urgent question: Could he order the targeted killing of an American citizen, in a country with which the United States was not at war, in secret and without the benefit of a trial?

> The Justice Department's Office of Legal Counsel prepared a lengthy memo justifying that extraordinary step, asserting that while the Fifth Amendment's guarantee of due process applied, it could be satisfied by internal deliberations in the executive branch.

> In the wake of Mr. Awlaki's death, some administration officials, including the attorney general, argued that the Justice Department's legal memo should be made public. In 2009, after all, Mr. Obama had released Bush administration legal opinions on interrogation over the vociferous objections of six former C.I.A. directors.

> This time, contemplating his own secrets, he chose to keep the Awlaki opinion secret.

94. **06-06-2012.**

95. **06-13-2012.**

96. **06-20-2012.** Michigan State Rep. Lisa Brown was barred from speaking in the House after telling Republicans, "I'm flattered you're all so concerned about my vagina. But no means no." In response, a perfomance of The Vagina Monologues was organized for the steps of the state Capitol; 2,500 people attended.

97. **06-27-2012.** In a ruling expected by no one—including me—the Supreme Court narrowly upheld the ACA, with John Roberts providing the swing vote. Which meant I had to scramble to write an entirely different cartoon than the one I had in mind if the law had been overturned. All in all, I didn't mind.

98. **07-04-2012.** The Court also doubled down on Citizens United, striking down a Montana law that limited corporate spending on elections.

99. **07-11-2012.** The first panel refers to the famous moment in the Reagan/Mondale debates, when Reagan sought to dispel doubts about his age and alertness (after a poor showing in the first debate) with, well, a clever one-liner some speechwriter had come up with. And it worked! Everyone agreed the clever one-liner certainly put those doubts to rest. It's particularly terrifying, given what we now know— the man was a few short years away from being diagnosed with Alzheimer's, and more to the point, his own son has speculated that he might have been in the early stages of the disease at that moment, and into his second term as President of the United States.

At the Republican Convention in 2004, delgates wore Band-Aids printed with small purple hearts as a way of mocking John Kerry's war injuries.

Teleprompters are discussed in endnote 77, above.

The week I wrote this cartoon, Mitt Romney had accused Barack Obama of being the real "outsourcer-in-chief."

100. **07-18-2012.** Romney couldn't discuss his time as governor because his signature achievement was the health care reform plan that Obamacare was modeled after. He couldn't discuss his Mormon faith because Christian evangelicals think Mormonism is a cult.

As I write this, he's bobbing and weaving to avoid releasing his tax returns, and he can't discuss his record as a businessperson due to Bain's history of predatory capitalism, even though his record as a businessperson is what he claims qualifies him for the presidency.

101. **08-15-2012.** Harry Reid said he'd been told by an anonymous source that Romney had paid no taxes for ten years. Politifact rated the statement a lie, because it could not be substantiated—setting off another round of debate about the standards by which the online truth squads declare something a falsehood. (The *Washington Post* factcheckers are actually the ones who use the Pinocchio scale mocked in this cartoon.)

102. **08-22-2012.** Ryan told *The Weekly Standard* in 2003, "I give out *Atlas Shrugged* as Christmas presents, and I make all my interns read it." In a 2005 speech, he said: "I grew up reading Ayn Rand and it taught me quite a bit about who I am, and what my value systems are, and what my beliefs are." In 2009 he posted a pro-Rand video on Facebook and wrote, "It's as if we're living in an Ayn Rand novel right now. I think Ayn Rand did the best job of anybody to build the moral case for capitalism." In 2012 he began to distance himself from Rand's atheism and pro-abortion beliefs, calling reports of his adherence to Objectivism an "urban legend" and invoking in her stead St. Thomas Aquinas, who wrote:

> *Man should not consider his material possession his own, but as common to all, so as to share them without hesitation when others are in need.*

103. **08-29-2012.** Congressman Todd Akin elicited a collective "WTF?" when he told an interviewer that victims of "legitimate rape" rarely get pregnant because "the female body has ways to try to shut that whole thing down." This turns out to be a common trope among anti-abortion extremists, allowing them an easy answer to the moral condundrum a raped, pregnant woman presents to pro-lifers. Republicans called on Akin to resign, apparently for the sin of saying out loud what they were thinking and becoming politically toxic in the process. That same week, the GOP platform committee adopted language calling for an end to abortion rights, with no exception for rape or incest. With the legal deadline for Akin to withdraw literally an hour away, Sean Hannity humiliated himself live on the air, all but begging Akin to drop out of the race. All of this drew attention to the fact that Akin's views (leaving aside the bit about rape-detecting uteruses) were largely indistinguishable from those of Republican vice presidential nominee Paul Ryan, with whom he had co-sponsored the "No Taxpayer Funding for Abortion Act" discussed in endnote 28.

Akin eventually acknowledged that he was "not a medical expert."

index

about the author

TOM TOMORROW'S NATIONALLY SYNDICATED political cartoon *This Modern World* appears online each week at Daily Kos and Truthout, and in alternative papers around the country. His cartoons and illustrations have been featured in *The New York Times, US News & World Report, The New Yorker, The American Prospect, The Nation, Spin, Esquire,* and on MSNBC's *Countdown with Keith Olbermann.* He was awarded the first place Robert F. Kennedy Journalism Award for Cartooning in 1998 and again in 2003. He has also been awarded the Media Alliance Meritorious Achievement Award for Excellence in Journalism, the Society of Professional Journalists' James Madison Freedom of Information Award, the James Aronson Award for Social Justice Journalism, and the Association for Education in Journalism Professional Freedom and Responsiblity Award.

In the early years of the George W. Bush administration, his work was adapted into a series of online animations, which can be viewed at *thismodernworld.com/animation-and-film*. He has been blogging since October of 2001, making him one of the earliest pioneers of the liberal blogosphere. He is the author of nine previous cartoon compilations and one book for children, and in 2009 collaborated with the band Pearl Jam to create the artwork for their album *Backspacer*.

A longtime resident of both San Francisco and Brooklyn, he currently lives just outside of New Haven, Connecticut with his wife and son.